CW00661194

CARE & REPAIR

Taking care of your home and its contents

CARE & REPAIR

Taking care of your home and its contents

Sixth Edition

GMC Publications

First published 1995 by
Guild of Master Craftsman Publications Ltd
166 High St, Lewes, East Sussex BN7 1XU

ISBN 0 946819 95 5

Illustration on page 9 © David James

The publishers can accept no legal responsibility for any consequences arising from the application
of information, advice or instructions given in this publication.

Designed and produced by Guild of Master Craftsman Publications Ltd
Printed by Ebenezer Baylis & Son Limited

This book has been compiled in response to the many enquiries received by The Guild of Master Craftsmen and is now in its sixth edition. It was formerly entitled 'Guide to Restoration Experts'.

The Guild was formed to look after the interests of craftspeople. The Guild actively promotes its members to the public, endeavouring always to see that both members and their customers are satisfied by its efforts.

Details of Guild membership may be obtained from:
The Secretary, The Guild of Master Craftsmen Ltd,
166 High St, Lewes, East Sussex. Telephone: (01273) 477374.

This publication lists both members and non-members of the Guild.

Contents

ORGANISATION OF ENTRIES

Entries are listed alphabetically under a specific category. Within each category entries are listed alphabetically by county and by name within each county. Entries for Ireland, Scotland and Wales appear at the end of the categories.

Features

Restoring books

Rachel Ward-sale

Bookbindings are fairly unusual, in that older examples are often in better condition than more recent ones. Early materials were of good quality: paper made from rag, and thick pieces of vegetable-tanned leather produced books which, while appearing crude, were exceptionally durable. Perversely, the desire for perfection led to a decline in standards – wood pulp replaced rag in paper, making it acidic and weak, and inferior quality leather was pared very thin, and then highly polished. These structural weaknesses led to bindings splitting after very little use.

Modern bookbinding developed in the fifteenth century following the introduction of paper making from China, and the invention of movable type. Books had been handwritten onto parchment, and bound with wooden boards which were attached to the pages with leather thongs, but the increasing demand for printed books brought a need for light and simple bindings – wooden boards were replaced with cardboard covered with decorated leather, and leather thongs were replaced with cord and linen thread.

The advent of machine binding in the nineteenth century produced a change in the design and binding of books. Until then, all books had been bound by hand, so each copy was unique. Machine binding meant that entire production runs were bound identically, usually in cloth covers, as leather was now reserved for special volumes and limited editions.

A good binding should open completely flat. Everyone must have experienced the frustrations of having to hold a book open with both hands, or trying to follow a recipe or music score when the book will not stay open. When repairing or re-binding a book, it is vital to retain or create a supple spine so that the book opens well for reading, while maintaining its shape and rigidity to look good on the shelf.

With cloth bindings this is fairly straightforward. The cover is removed and the old layers of muslin (mull) and paper are taken from the spine. The stitching is then made sound and, if necessary, new tapes or cords are attached before a new layer of mull and paper are applied. A new cover is then made, or the original restored for re-use, and the book is glued back in using the hollow spine technique. With this technique, the spine of the book is not connected to the spine of the cover – this enables the cover spine to retain its convex shape when opened, while the book spine becomes concave.

Repairing a leather-bound book can be somewhat different. The hollow spine technique has been used on leather bindings from the nineteenth century onwards, but earlier books were made with a tight back, with the covering leather stuck directly onto the spine of the book, usually moulded over raised cards. As the leather was often attached with hot glue, the spines tended to be very rigid and hard to open, and removing such spines for re-

Leather used in restoring old covers can be matched very well with the original.

use is virtually impossible. With tight back books, the spine has to be discarded, and as much old glue as possible removed. The old boards are then re-attached, using un-bleached linen for strength and flexibility. A new piece of leather is used to re-cover the spine, with the edges tucked under the origi-nal leather on the boards. With careful choice and dyeing of leather, a very good match can be achieved.

Repairing a hollow spine on a leather bind-ing is generally easier. Because the spine is sep-arate from the book, it can be removed with all its decoration and a new leather spine applied, again, separate from the book. The old spine can then be stuck over the new leather. This is probably the most successful repair, as only a small amount of new leather remains visible,

and this can be dyed and polished to match the original.

A well-bound book should be a pleasure to read, and with care, should last many years. Keep books out of direct sunlight which rots the bindings, and fit bookshelves to inside walls to avoid the risk of damp. Leather bind-ings benefit from regular handling, as oil from the hands helps keep the leather supple. To restore or maintain the surface, leather dress-ings and waxes are available from bookbind-ing suppliers. Above all, do not use adhesive tapes to repair books or their bindings, as adhesive remains on the pages even if the tape is removed, staining and weakening them. Torn pages are better mended with strips of tis-sue paper (preferably Japanese mending tis-sue) and water-based paste.

Restoring rocking horses

Clive Green

Rocking horses have been around for hundreds of years and remain favourite playthings for children. It is in the nature of children's playthings that they are often roughly used and abused, and that children outgrow them. Nevertheless, a surprising number of rocking horses survive – often stored away, neglected, in some attic, shed or barn.

The beauty of the wooden rocking horse is that, whatever state it is in, it can usually be restored by any reasonably practical person. A modest tool kit, together with time, effort and money, will achieve a satisfactory result.

Although many old or battered horses are not of great monetary worth, and have no antique value to be destroyed by inept restoration, they may well have great sentimental value. You could, therefore, spend more time and money on your rocking horse's restoration than it is currently worth. Let it be a labour of love, and enjoy giving your battered old horse a new lease of life, with the bonus that old

Clive Green with rocking horses ready for restoration. Both are circa 1930s.

rocking horses are becoming increasingly sought, and their price is rising all the time.

Ten tips to make restoring rocking horses easier

* Plan what you want to do. Do you want to do the minimum of work necessary to make the horse safe and presentable? Sometimes this is all that is necessary or desirable. You may, however, wish to go the whole hog and produce what is almost a new rocking horse.

* Always take photographs before you start work. By doing so, you will not only have a record of the colour of your horse and any special markings you may want to repeat on your finished horse, but you will also have a record of the excellent work you have done in restoring it.

* When you take the horse off the stand or rocker, mark one of the legs and make a corresponding mark on the stand or rocker so that you are sure to get the horse back the right way round. This may sound daft, but legs have been cracked in trying to put a horse back on its stand the wrong way – bolt holes for the horses are rarely equidistant.

* Use as much of the original material as you can to preserve the historical integrity of the horse: stirrups, bits, brackets, bolts and swing irons are usually reusable if they are present. You may even be able to reuse some of the fancy nails if you take care when removing them. Keep the saddle so that you can either copy it yourself, or get a professional to make a new one for you.

* If the eyes are made of glass, take great care not to scuff or scratch them with abrasive paper during restoration. If you feel there is any danger of doing this, remove them and keep them to one side. It is a simple job to replace them

when you have finished all the other work, and that shiny glint in the eye is all-important.

* Do not hurry. Restoring a rocking horse requires time and patience, and, of course, money! Do not spoil the job by rushing it. It is also a dirty and dusty job, so try to find somewhere suitable to work. Preferably a place where you will not have to tidy everything away after each working session.

* If you use power rotary sanding devices for stripping paint and gesso, do be careful. It is easy to cause great damage very quickly. If you must use mechanical means, use a foam-padded rotary sander – steer clear of disc sanders. Also, use a good face mask and goggles: many old horses were painted with lead paint! If you decide to replace the original gesso, you will need to make this up using whiting and rabbit skin glue.

* Cascamite is probably the best glue to use for repairs, though Evo-Stik waterproof glue gives a strong bond. For small repairs, such as minor chips out of the ears, Superglue is quick and effective.

* If, as is often the case, the tops of the ears are worn and chipped, you may decide that these add character to the horse and leave them, but, whatever you do, do not neglect the stand or rocker. Loose or wobbly stands and rockers are the cause of many cracked and broken legs. Make sure the stands and rockers are strong and firm.

Further reading

Restoring Rocking Horses by Clive Green and Anthony Dew is available from GMC Publications, or from any good book shop. Clive Green may be contacted at 20 Broadmark Lane, Rustington, West Sussex, BN16 2HJ. Telephone: 01903 786639.

Building maintenance and restoration

Tony Barrell

When construction turned into architecture, we were left with an endless maintenance schedule for our beautiful, but decaying buildings. It was the Renaissance that did it. Where British buildings had once been sensible, functional things for living and working in, they suddenly started conforming to reclaimed rules of proportion, and sprouting flourishes to convince passers-by that they had strayed into ancient Rome, Greece, Egypt or some other place. After that, our buildings could never be just buildings again; they were works of art.

When our earliest timber-framed hovels rotted away (because they had been plonked

This house is, in fact, a new construction filling in a passage, but it replicates the style of its neighbours with great success. It can be done!

straight onto earth where they quickly became feasts for indigenous fungus and wood-boring beetles), there was no Society for the Protection of Ancient Buildings to bemoan their passing, and new structures were simply put up to replace them. But, now that old buildings have an artistic life beyond human needs for shelter and security, they have to be preserved for the nation like priceless paintings and sculptures.

Initially, this new way of looking at buildings applied exclusively to big, important works like the grand residences of the well-to-do, but it did not take long to filter down and encompass much humbler structures, like farmhouses and artisan's cottages. The simple robustness and charm of thatch, wattle and daub, cleft oak, rubblestone and handmade red brick soon became an important part of the English ideal, and it became acceptable to be judgmental about the commonplace. The painter Helen Allingham, for example, would often override reality for some of her romantic cottage scenes, by depicting traditional lattice windows where they had, in fact, been replaced by larger modern panes.

The problem we are faced with in preserving buildings, and particularly those that are homes, is that they were built to protect us, and they have to withstand some of the least clement weather in the world. It's like asking the Mona Lisa or the Venus de Milo to put up

White mortar has been artlessly trowelled over the walls of this cottage to give it the rustic appearance of random stone.

with a random succession of attacks with bucketfuls of water and ice, powerful hair dryers, and bright tungsten lights. Moreover, we actually live in the buildings, and we are notoriously accident-prone, not to mention keen on DIY. Under constant attack from within and without, our buildings need an awful lot of maintenance and protection to keep them from dereliction and mistreatment. Unfortunately, we can't all be willing and able curators of these precious structures; most of us don't have the funds, the time or the skills.

This conjunction of artistic worth and vulnerability is at its most poignant in the case of old houses. For many, their fate depends on the owners who, essentially, fall into three groups:
◆ the restorers: those who give their time to restoring their Edwardian, Victorian, Georgian, or pre-Georgian house 'to its former glory';
◆ the campers: those who take their houses as they find them. While they don't do anything

to damage or compromise the building, nor do they attempt to arrest its day-to-day decay; and
◆ the bodgers: those who don't see their buildings as having artistic value, but as being purely functional structures. They may adapt them with results that can be described most politely as 'individualistic'. Handsome period features are replaced by the latest fads and labour-saving devices, solid, proud, well-designed front doors are removed to fit blocks of hardwood and well-made sash windows, complementing the house's facade, make way for aluminium or UPVC frames – and that's just the outside.

Bodgers cause no end of bother for the architectural conservationist. While lack of funds can prohibit restoration, it is not the cause of bodging – it can cost just as much for a bodger to ruin a terraced objet d'art as it does for a restorer to do it justice, while restoring a bodged job can cost even more.

The problems of redecoration

Jacqueline Duncan

*Jacqueline Duncan, Principal, founded the Inchbald School of Design in 1960.
The department of Design History is run by Mrs Diana Lloyd.*

In the aftermath of WWII, England lost a significant part of her architectural heritage. Happily, we awoke to the destruction before it was too late: the Georgian Society, the National Trust, the Irish Georgian Society and the Victorian Society have all contributed to the saving of English architectural heritage. They, and other bodies like them, have generated public interest and education, and encouraged the owners of old houses to study the style and fabric of their buildings before embarking on extensive, and perhaps unsympathetic refurbishment.

I have avoided the word 'preservation'. In my view, architects build houses for people, not posterity. I am not of the purist school that would restore a house to its original state, without regard to contemporary needs. A house or cottage built in the eighteenth century may not suit the demands of the twentieth century – buildings must adapt to the passage of time.

The policy of total preservation is a new trend, and can frequently inhibit refurbishment plans, particularly those of the interior. A balance is needed between preserving at all costs, and exercising an informed judgement as to the desirability of so doing.

For the owner who is anxious to restore their house to a standard consistent with a modern lifestyle, without damaging its inherent character, the first step is to establish the style of architecture, and identify the fabrics used in the building. If it is possible to find or reconstruct an original plan, it will be easier to clarify the extent of later additions or alterations. With that knowledge, and an appreciation of the correct period, the choice of suitable materials is made more obvious. Local products always have a profound influence on local building, so local knowledge is vital to those seeking authenticity.

It is impossible to expand fully on this subject in the space of a short article. It is worth noting here, however, that the interest generated in restoration and conservation in recent years has given a tremendous impetus to the redevelopment of the craftsman's skill, a skill almost destroyed in the industrial and educational upheavals of WWII. As a result, it is now possible to call on craftsmen's expertise in every area: where finance restricts this, enthusiastic owners should be aware that a cautious approach is vital.

Never strip paint or wallpaper until it has been carefully scraped to see what has gone before. Check curtain styles for the type of house being restored, and further, check the kind of materials that might have been used originally, or that would be suitable substitutes now. It is not necessary to be too purist: the cottages of 200 years ago would hardly have had the kind of decoration we favour today, but it is possible to preserve the cottage simplicity and have rather more luxurious window treatments than an eighteenth-century shepherd's wife could have afforded or justified!

There are few rules regarding furnishings that cannot be broken, but always with care. In general, it is better to use furniture that is contemporary with, or subsequent to the period of the house. As an extreme example, Tudor furniture would look out of place in an overtly Regency room, but curiously, the elegance of Regency furniture is enhanced by a modest background.

Upholstery faces more fashionable swings than almost any other aspect of decoration: subject to fads and new developments, it can quickly become outdated, and thus be a greater giveaway than the furniture itself. Much more attention has been paid to the subject recently, and one result of this is that the contours of antique chairs can be restored accurately, and their comfort enhanced by modern techniques. The exhuberant upholstery of the nineteenth century has enjoyed a revival, and much attention is now given to appropriate fabrics and finishings.

I have not touched lighting! The lighting technology of the twentieth century can add an extra dimension to an old interior, but remember, if you choose original colours, they were not intended to be flooded with low halogen light.

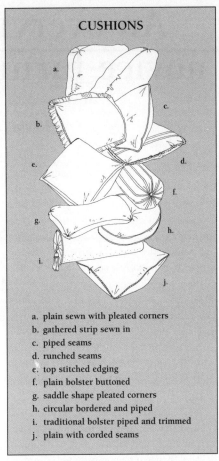

CUSHIONS

a. plain sewn with pleated corners
b. gathered strip sewn in
c. piped seams
d. runched seams
e. top stitched edging
f. plain bolster buttoned
g. saddle shape pleated corners
h. circular bordered and piped
i. traditional bolster piped and trimmed
j. plain with corded seams

The fashion in cushions and accessories is constantly changing.

The greatest problem facing the enthusiastic restorer is that interior decoration is a composite art. Knowledge of all the technical and artistic skills that go into the decoration of houses is required, and here the craftsman comes into his own. How nearly we lost him, how little we value his services, and with what difficulty does he educate himself in this modern world, with the apprentice system apparently gone for good.

An overview for the novice furniture restorer

Kevin Jan Bonner

It was while waiting for inspiration that I read an article revealing the new concept in marketing – personification. Imagining a product as a person seemed an interesting idea: how about personifying furniture restoration? What sort of person would it be? Without doubt, furniture restoration has to be represented by two people, or at the very least, a split personality.

The first person, Antique Restoration, is old, imperious and crusty – a Dame Agatha with a blue rinse and pearls. She is traditional, fussy, dogmatic, disciplined, pedantic, and steeped in the past. She does not suffer fools gladly, but is highly respected for her wisdom and aristocratic bearing. Her middle name is definitely History.

The second person, Junk Restoration, is a lot younger (middle thirties), modern – perhaps an Aunty Zoe, with red hair, jeans and trainers. Iconoclastic, gauche, experimental, disrespectful and inclined to upset the pompous and staid, she is a lot easier to get on with than Dame Agatha, and a lot more fun. Her middle name could be Fashion.

Whatever the differences, it is the same blood that runs through these veins – they are very closely related. They both use similar materials, processes and techniques, but their attitude to life is opposed.

Antique restoration is concerned with restoring old and valuable furniture to its original condition. Ideally, it employs the skills, materials, and finishes that were used when the furniture was first created. Old animal glues, French polishes, waxes and oils are used, and working methods and recipes that have been passed down through the generations are glorified, while anything modern and newfangled is rejected.

Junk restoration does not give a hoot for tradition or for the furniture's origins. It is interested in creating a useful and decorative piece of furniture from what was formerly a piece of worthless, unwanted junk. Any method, finish or technique will be considered: if it works, do it.

I suppose midway between these two lies the true face of furniture restoration. The best, most flexible restorers will, of course, keep the company of both ladies. Whether you defer to Dame Agatha or Aunty Zoe is largely dependent on the nature of the furniture you choose to restore, and on the brief. Does it need French polishing or painting green? What would look best? What would be in keeping with the style of the furniture? What would improve it? These and dozens of other questions will determine the persona you adopt. Each project is different, and each will determine a slightly different approach, a slightly different balance of Dame Agatha and Aunty Zoe.

Whatever the final choice of approach, one thing is guaranteed; furniture restoration

Restoration brings out the character of the furniture, and can reflect that of the craftsman as well.

draws upon a vast range of skills. This is the common denominator and the fascination of the craft. There are literally hundreds of skills, experiences and techniques to acquire. Many of them need only the application of a little common sense to learn, but some will take years of dedicated practice to master.

When describing the craft to my pupils, I often compare it to learning a musical instrument. At first you learn the basics, playing a few simple tunes and making mistakes as you slowly develop your skills and knowledge. Eventually, after many years of practice, you are able to play the most complicated pieces without fault. If you have an interest in restoration, and are willing to spend a little time and energy, this is the way to learn it. Buy a good book to guide you, find a piece of junk, and start

playing. Junk is certainly the place for the amateur to start: strip it, fix it, stain it, polish it – don't worry! Enjoy it! Use junk to pick up the basics and then progress to antique restoration.

If, after all this encouragement, explanation and enthusing, you decide to let someone else do the work for you, if the prospect of all the toxic gunge, tired arms and putrid pong is too much and you decide to employ the services of an experienced restorer, don't begrudge them their pittance – they have spent a long time and a lot of energy gaining their skills. More importantly, if you become attuned to the finer points of the craft, each time you look at your newly restored furniture you may catch a few bars of the furniture restorer's music. Whether it be pop from Aunty Zoe or a concerto from Dame Agatha, if it has melody it is priceless.

Creating a garden

Mike Coote

Gardening is, in essence, simple. It can be done by anyone, and can be one of the most satisfying of hobbies. Plants are rewarding in so many ways, repaying many times over the care required to grow them. Think of the years of pleasure you will get from a cherry tree costing a few pounds, and taking perhaps half a day to plant. Or the delicious fresh food you can get from a small vegetable patch. Or the brilliantly coloured annuals you can get from a few pennies worth of seed – the outlay will be nothing the following year because the plant will provide the seeds for you, and if you take the seeds from the plants with the best flowers you can create your own strain, ideally suited to your garden.

As with anything, there are certain fundamental principles which must be followed, but nowhere are they more widely ignored than in the garden. The first principle is patience. *Patience.* When you take over a garden you must wait an entire growing season before you change anything. If you move in in September, this means waiting a year, but you will by no means be idle during this year. You will be looking at the garden from every angle, deciding what you want it to be, what you want to do in it, how much time you want to spend working in it, or sitting in it. Are there ugly views you want to hide, or beautiful views you want to enhance? You will be visiting lots of local gardens, noting the plants you like, and talking to the owners to find out if they are easy to grow or get hold of – politely refusing

offers of plants this year, your planning year, but next year, yes please. You will be looking over the garden fence to see what is doing well there, and talking to your neighbour.

Another major task for the year is identifying the plants which are already growing in the garden. This is easier than you think. Take a bit when you go garden visiting, ask the neighbours, or join the Royal Horticultural Society, a bargain at £30 a year, and they will do it for you. What you are looking for in this first year is not the good guys, nor any rarities left by previous gardeners, although they are of course good to find, what you are looking for is the baddies, the perennial weeds. These you must seek and destroy. This is the second fundamental principle of gardening – kill perennial weeds. It is the difference between years of pleasure in the garden, and years of hassle. Weeds can be destroyed with chemicals, or by excluding the light from an infested area for a growing season by covering it with black polythene, or, very laboriously, destroyed by hand. What is essential is that you are quite sure you have been successful before you plant anything.

It may seem odd that I am suggesting a year of inactivity and killing as a first step in creating a garden, but you really will gain immeasurably if you take this advice.

The final element in this first year is design. This should not be something done by someone else to your garden. If it is to be successful, it can only be done by you. This doesn't mean

Cherry tree in blossom.

not to employ a designer, only that if you are to be satisfied, they need to do what you tell them to do, and you need to decide what you want. If you invest in some bamboo canes, they can be used to represent trees, and moved around until they are in just the right place. Hosepipe can be used to mark the edge of flower beds or shrub borders. Sit on your proposed terrace, with a glass of wine, and imagine how the garden will be. You can even move the terrace around, trying it in different places. In this first year, nothing is fixed. It is the time to crystallise your ideas and build up your strength – next year you will have a lot to do.

The Royal Horticultural Society Membership Dept can be contacted on 0171 821 3000.

Gardens of England and Wales is published annually by the National Gardens Scheme and gives details of nearly 3000 private gardens.

Gaillardia flowering in October.

Unnecessary costs in home improvements

David Booth

David Booth is a Chartered Building Surveyor.

Sympathy is what we give to a friend or relative who is ill and in need of some treatment, but it is often missing when we 'improve' or repair our property. Knocking down walls, taking out fireplaces, or adding a lumpy flat-roofed extension can often seriously damage the aesthetic health of a house!

Very often, especially if you have just moved house, you want to get to work immediately. Only when you have finished the work do you realise it might have been better done another way. So, before you start wielding the sledge-hammer, spend a little time planning. Firstly, why do you want to make the improvement? Is it to add space, update a kitchen or bathroom, or alter the existing accommodation plan? Whatever it is, look carefully at the alternatives.

If you want more space, a loft conversion can generally give more bedroom space, while an extension can give more living space. There may also be ways of getting what you want through swapping rooms. If you have a large bathroom and need a double bedroom, it may be possible to move the bathroom into a single bedroom and turn the old bathroom into a double bedroom. This operation can be a lot less expensive than a loft conversion.

Your proposed improvement may require planning approval, so check with your local planning department before starting any work. If you do start before checking and they then refuse the planning application, they can make you return the building to its original state – an expensive mistake! If the improvements involve structural work they will have to comply with current building regulations – again, check with your local building control department.

Another important aspect to consider is the value the work will add to the house. I have often seen houses on which a lot of money has been spent that will not be recovered when the house is sold. Remember, the value of the house is not just based on the house and how it looks, but also, and very importantly, where it is. Most streets have a ceiling price, and it is worth talking to a local estate agent to see if the money you will be spending will add to the value of your home.

Over the years, houses have been built using different materials and different methods of construction. Up until the 1930s, most houses had solid brick external walls and little or no damp proof courses. Earlier still, timber was sometimes used in the fabric of the external walls, and even some clay and chalk houses are still standing. Since the 1930s, cavity walls have been introduced, and in recent developments, timber-framed houses have been built. It is important to make any improvements in sympathy with the original structure, and to use materials and building methods that are compatible.

As with our health, prevention is better, and a lot cheaper than cure. However, while we may get over a bout of 'flu, a house cannot mend itself: if there is a problem, it will only get worse and more expensive to repair. Maintaining your property is important. A leaking gutter, especially on a solid-walled building, can lead to permeating damp, wet, or even dry rot. To repair the gutter would probably cost under £100, while remedial treatment for dry rot can cost thousands. On a regular basis, check your gutters and down-pipes for any leaks or spills, check the roof for any slipped tiles, check that your loft and any pipework is insulated, and that there are no areas of light shining through the roof. Redecorate earlier rather than putting it off for another year.

I spend a lot of my time with clients discussing their ideas for improving their homes, and then draw up a specification with a schedule of work precisely detailing all the items to be completed. This schedule can then be given to contractors who will quote on a like for like basis. When the contract is awarded, any extra work can be clearly identified and costed on a similar basis. Contractors often request stage payments, and these can be more easily assessed from the costed schedule of works. It is recommended that payment be made only for work completed and materials on site, and a contract referring to the schedule, stage payments, and a date of completion will help protect both the client and the contractor.

While aluminium windows may be excellent draught-free replacements for sash windows, they do not always sit happily with older windows surrounding them.

Maintaining and updating household utilities

David Booth

David Booth is a Chartered Building Surveyor.

Household utilities provide the services that come into the house (electricity, gas, telephone, and water), and also those that go out (rainwater and sewage). While most of them are now privatised, you don't usually have much choice in the suppliers. However, there are ways of saving money: here are a few co ments on the services most likely to come into or go out of your home.

Electricity

This is normally supplied by your local Electricity Board. The distribution board (also called a fuse box) is often in the understairs cupboard and contains the meter and the consumer unit. Newer installations have an external meter. Older consumer units have wired fuses, and if they blow you have to re-wire them, so it is useful to keep a torch nearby. Re-wiring must always be done with fuse wire, and the correct rating must be used. More recent units have miniature circuit breakers (MCBs). Instead of removable wired fuses, they have switches that turn off if the circuit has been overloaded. If this happens, you simply turn the MCB back on. In addition, you may have a Residual Current Device (RCD) fitted, and this cuts out if there is any leakage of current to earth, as occurs when a live cable is cut.

If any of these devices continue to fail and you are unsure of the cause, call in a qualified electrician to investigate the problem. What continues to amaze me is that there are no laws (apart from the Common Law of Negligence) that control electrical installations or electrical engineers. If a plumber makes a mistake you might get a little wet, but an electrical mistake can be a lot more serious. The Institute of Electrical Engineers produces recommendations and guidelines for electrical installations – if you have your property re-wired, insist on an IEE completion certificate. The institute can be contacted on 0171 240 1871.

Gas

All gas installations or alterations must be carried out by a CORGI-registered engineer (although you are allowed to blow yourself up!). If someone is paid to work on a gas installation and they are not registered, they can be prosecuted. CORGI can be contacted on 01256 708133. If you are not on main line gas, Liquid Petroleum Gas (LPG) can be installed, but this can prove more expensive for heating than main line gas and more even than some electrical installations.

Telephone

There are now alternatives to British Telecom. Mercury claim to save money on long distance calls, and access to the telephone network via cable television claims to be cheaper still. Be sure, however, to include any extra line rentals, initial connection charges, and call charges in your calculations to find the real cost.

Water

Water charges appear to be going up and up: check to see if installing a water meter will save you money.

Rainwater

In older properties, and in areas where the ground has very dense clay, the rainwater is usually connected to the main sewage system. If not, it will probably be led to a soakaway. This is basically a hole in the ground filled with rubble, into which the water is piped and left to soak away. You have probably seen large concrete cylinders with holes in their sides next to roadworks: these are soakaways for rainwater draining from roads.

Foul sewage

Not a pleasant subject, but a very necessary one. Most homes in or near cities and towns are connected to main line sewage systems. As long as your pipes aren't blocked, you have little to worry about. If you live in the country, however, you may have a cesspool or a septic tank. A cesspool is a tank in the ground where the sewage is held until it is collected by a sewage services contractor. A septic tank breaks down the sewage naturally by means of anaerobic bacteria. This produces a sludge at the bottom which will eventually need removing, and a relatively clear liquid at the top which is discharged through land drains. While a septic tank

Avoid unnecessary clutter!

requires emptying every six to twelve months, a cesspool needs emptying on a much more regular basis. As emptying charges are continually increasing, it may be more economical to change to a septic tank if you have a cesspool.

Blacksmithing: restoring ironwork

Andrew and Lyn Hall

Andrew Hall works at the Forge in the village of Branscombe in Devon. The Forge is owned by the National Trust and is one of the few working thatched forges remaining in Great Britain. Andrew won the title of International Live Blacksmith in 1993.

The modern blacksmith should be capable of undertaking a range of tasks, from very fine work such as leaf work, repoussé, and flowers made from plate steel, to heavy work including large ornate gates and railings, and heavy industrial work on such things as anchors and D-shackles.

There is a growing tendency to treat ironwork as a piece of art, so that in its restoration, it is cleaned up and has any sharp edges and rust removed, but any pieces that are missing or that are are badly rusted are not replaced. In my opinion, a blacksmith skilled in his craft should replace worn parts and return the ironwork to its original state, or as near to it as possible. One of the main problems with this is that nearly all the old decorative ironwork was made from wrought iron, of which there is a limited supply today, and while most items made from wrought iron can be made with mild steel, it corrodes much faster than wrought iron. Where mild steel continues to oxidise and corrode as long as it is exposed to the elements, wrought iron is made up of layers, and though the first layer may corrode, the underlying layers remain protected.

The most important task when undertaking restorative work, is to make a close inspection of the piece, taking as many photographs as necessary and making drawings of some of the more intricate and difficult to photograph pieces. It is important to be aware that there is always more work to be done than can at first be seen, and these photos will be very useful later. Before removing the piece from its site, measurements of fixing points must be taken, i.e. hinge centres, post centres, larch points etc.

When taking down and dismantling the piece, take care to keep its shape and to protect any delicate parts. Once dismantled, any rust and old paint can be removed by burning off and scraping with a wire brush.

This is the stage at which a full report on damage and corrosion can be made, and a price for restoration estimated. It is also the time to decide by which process to restore the piece. If there are panels which have leaf work, repoussé, flowers or small scroll work that has rusted away, these should be re-made. Any structural parts that have rusted and weakened the piece should also be re-made. When all the individual pieces have been repaired, they can

Andrew Hall at work in Branscombe forge.

be re-assembled by the traditional methods of fixing, using such things as rivets, mortice and tenon joints, nuts and bolts, and dowels.

Where paint is to be used to protect the piece, it is important to start with a good zinc primer. Methods used for cleaning the iron-work will depend upon the delicacy of the piece. If the piece is not too delicate, it can be shot-blasted, and then zinc primed immediately to avoid oxidisation of the metal surface. If the work is very fine, heat along with rotary and hand wire brushes should be used prior to zinc priming. Any additional undercoats should be applied in the workshop, but the top coat should be left until the piece is back on site and re-erected. This avoids any damage occurring during transit and assembly.

There are a number of other finishes that can

be used, each with their own advantages and disadvantages. Galvanising gives mild steel a good protection against the elements, but pro-duces a very heavy layer which can hide fine details. It cannot be used on wrought iron as it tends to lift the layers, causing faster corrosion. Tinning is good on small, fine items as it gives a good protective coat without the heavy layer that painting and galvanising leave. Electro-plating, a modern process, can be used in the same way as tinning.

When re-erecting the piece on site, it should be fixed by such processes as lead corking, molten lead, or anchor bolts and screws. Once the piece is standing, it can be finished with a coat of high quality metal paint. If the piece is then maintained properly, it should not require any further restorative work.

Directory

Helpful organisations
Publications index

ANTIQUE RESTORATION

Berkshire

HAMILTON HAVERS
Reading RG4 7JE
Tel: 01734 473379

Specialist in marquetry, boulle, brass, inlays, old ivory and tortoiseshell, French polishing, mother-of-pearl, ormolu and marble. On furniture, clock cases and objects of art. All work is executed to the highest standard. Nationwide service to historic houses, private collectors, museums and the trade. By appointment only.

Lincolnshire

E. CZAJKOWSKI & SON
96 Tor-o-Moor Road,
Woodhall Spa LN10 6SB
Tel: 01526 352895

Operating nationally, this well-established firm specialises in two main areas: a) restoration of antique furniture, clocks and barometers, including lacquer work, decorated finishes, carving, gilding and marquetry; b) designing individually handmade furniture to complement existing modern or antique furniture. Exact copies can be made of original pieces if required. **M**

London

CARVERS & GILDERS
9 Charterhouse Works,
Eltringham Street SW18
Tel: 0181 870 7047/Fax: 0181 874 0470

Restorers of fine eighteenth-century carved and gilded furniture and mirror frames. Wherever possible, original structures and surfaces are retained. Traditional techniques and materials are used and any new work is meticulously matched to the original. By appointment only. **M**

TIMOTHY NAYLOR ASSOCIATES
The Workshop, 2 Chertsey Road,
Chobham GU24 8NB
Tel: 01276 855122 **M**

Yorkshire (South)

T.F.R. (Mr J. Tibbs)
43 Standon Crescent, Sheffield S9 1PN
Tel: 0114 2422364

French polishing, traditional and modern finishes, carving, cleaning. Particularly concerned with repair and restoration of wooden furniture, modern and antique, yet equally happy to provide the above finishes for doors, staircases and panelling. Free quotations.

M

Yorkshire (West)

G.R.T. SERVICES (G. R. Thombs)
16 Gordon Street, Linthwaite,
Huddersfield HD7 5LN
Tel: 01484 844037 (office)
01484 847805 (works)

Over 30 years experience offering French polishing, antique repair and restoration, veneering, woodturning and carving. Cabinet makers, chairs etc., plus upholstery. Furniture made to customer's design and style. Commission work undertaken. On site work carried out to doors, panelling, staircases and ecclesiastical work. First class tradesmen, nationwide service.

BOOKBINDERS

Hampshire

R. A. & E. J. WHITE

27 Preston Road, North End,
Portsmouth PO2 7JT
Tel: 01705 668364

Handbinding of all kinds of books.
Theses a speciality.

M

Oxfordshire

MICHAEL'S BINDERY
49 Curtis Avenue,
Abingdon OX14 3UL
Tel: 01235 526072

Hand bookbinder and gold finisher since 1967. Any type of book bound – journals, theses, magazines, etc. Single or multiple copies. Repairs and restoration of old books and bibles, old lettering, personalisation on christening books, wallets, handbags, identity labels. Wide choice of materials available. Free estimates given. **M**

ARTEFACTS AND COLLECTABLES

CERAMICS

Hampshire

MARY ROSE WRANGHAM
25 St Martin's House,
Clarence Parade, Southsea,
Portsmouth PO5 2EZ
Tel: 01705 829863

An experienced restorer who has worked for dealers for 22 years. Free estimates given. Specialising in English, continental porcelains and oriental Chinese-style decorative repairs of Ming (circa 1400) in gold leaf. Ceramic restoration courses available – see Courses, on page 51, for full details. **M**

Suffolk

MADELEINE BECK, RESTORER OF PORCE-LAIN & POTTERY
Evergreen, Barningham,
Bury-St-Edmunds IP31 1DD
Tel: 01359 221558

Friendly personal service for restoration of antique or modern ceramics. Breaks and cracks mended, stains removed, missing pieces remade etc. Free estimates and advice. **M**

Surrey

NORMAN FLYNN RESTORATIONS
37 Lind Road, Sutton SM1 4PP
Tel: 0181 661 9505

Established 1972. An experienced team of artists specialising in the restoration of antique porcelain, pottery and enamels, serving some of the best London dealers and clients from all over the world. Also lamp conversions. **M**

CLOCKS & BAROMETERS

London

NEWCOMBE & SON (Mike Newcombe)
89 Maple Road, Penge SE20 8UL
Tel: 0181 778 0816

Specialists in making, repair and restoration. Quality clock cases made to order, barometers repaired, silvering, gilding, clock faces repainted, enamel restored. Brass and wood frets, clock hands all hand cut and finished to order. Clocks bought and sold.

Yorkshire (South)

WOODEN WONDERS (B. Webb)
342 Bawtry Road, Hellaby,
Rotherham S66 8EY
Tel: 01709 548508

Long case, wall and bracket clocks made to commission. All cases are handmade using good quality timber to ensure satisfaction for future generations. Restoration of cases undertaken. **M**

GLASS DECORATION

Berkshire

GLASS DESIGN & DECORATION LTD
39 Longshot Lane, Bracknell RG12 1RL
Tel: 01344 485763/Fax: 01344 485763

All types of surface treatments on all types of flat glass. Sandblast, acid etching or combination of both, gilding, painting, including ceramic. Suitable for private or business houses and public buildings, functional or decorative. Free estimates given by phone or fax. Advice given – 100 years experience. **M**

Oxfordshire

PHILIP LAWSON JOHNSTON
307 Woodstock Road, Oxford OX2 7NY
Tel: 01865 515417/Fax: 01865 54104

Specialist hand engraving to commission. Company logos, inscriptions, wildlife scenes, heraldic, buildings, plus large-scale windows, doors, table tops and panels. Quotations given. **M**

MODEL MAKERS

Lancashire

C.C.W. MODEL MANUFACTURING CO
Unit 10, Tyldesley House, Elliott Street,
Tyldesley, Manchester M29 8DS
Tel/Fax: 01942 896138

Manufacturers of fine scale 'O' gauge locomotive kits and complete models. Also undertake industrial model making, facilities for white metal castings, lost wax and cast iron. **M**

PICTURE RESTORERS AND FRAMERS

Avon

DAVID CROSS GALLERY
7 Boyces Avenue, Clifton,
Bristol BS8 4AA
Tel: 0117 9732614

Picture restoration. Oil paintings, relining, cleaning; paper conservation and retouching of water colours and prints, mounting and treating of time-staining. Framing and fitting of all types of paintings. Rebuilding of antique decorative and wood frames; gold leaf and gilding, colouring and stressing to personal instruction and requirements.

Lancashire

RICHARD ZAHLER
Lane House, Fowgill,
Bentham, Lancaster LA2 7AH
Tel: 01524 261998

Restoring and cleaning of easel paintings, pastels, polychrome sculptures, mural and ceiling paintings, icons, prints, drawings, watercolours, maps, oriental works of art, architectural drawings. Picture relining by traditional and modern methods. Water and oil gilding; repair and restoration of frames. **M**

London

JOHN CAMPBELL PICTURE FRAMES LTD
164 Walton Street SW3 2JL
Tel: 0171 584 9268/Fax: 0171 581 3499

'Master framing with a touch of genius'. Campbell's of Walton Street are also experts in carving, gilding, restoring picture frames, oil paintings and works on paper. More than 250 years of collective experience is available.

PAUL MITCHELL LTD
99 New Bond Street W1Y 9LF
Tel: 0171 493 8732

Established 1928, specialising in the restoration and conservation of oil paintings. Free advice is offered on the condition of pictures, and for proposed auction purposes. Expert picture framers, holding an extensive stock of antique frames of all schools. Workshops produce hand-carved and gilded replicas. **M**

ROCKING HORSES

Sussex (West)

CLIVE GREEN
The Lychgate, 20 Broadmark Lane,
Rustington BN16 2HJ
Tel: 01903 786639

Member of the British Toymakers Guild from whom an award for excellence has been received. Maker and restorer of carved wooden rocking horses. **M**

Wales - Clwyd

STUART & PAM McPHERSON A.P.E.S
Rocking Horses: Designers, Makers
& Restorers
Ty Gwyn, Llannefyd, Denbigh LL16 5HB
Tel: 0174 579365

Rocking horse makers/restorers, established 1978. Original, limited edition British ponies, unicorns, gallopers in rideable and miniature (1/12th scale) versions, plus traditional carved wooden horses. Commission work. Restoration/conservation of old horses.

Photographs available. British Toymakers Guild. U.K.I.C. listed on the Conservation Unit Register of the Museums and Galleries Commission.

STAINED GLASS ARTISTS

Avon

JOSEPH BELL & SON

68 Park Street, Bristol BS1 5JX
Tel: 0117 9268543

Stained glass artists established 1840. As well as designing and making new windows, we have, over the years, developed skilled restoration and conservation techniques for every kind of stained glass window, from medieval to modern. We also make, restore and repair leaded lights of all descriptions. Areas covered: West Country, South Wales and South-West Midlands.

M

Cheshire

ILLUMIN GLASS STUDIO
Ian Baillie
82 Bond Street, Macclesfield SK11 6QS
Tel: 01625 613600

Design, manufacture, repair and installation of stained glass windows and lighting to customer's own requirements. Fitting of leaded lights into double glazing. Supply of decorative and antique sheet glass and glass decoration (e.g. bevelling, etching etc.).Renovation and repair of antique light fittings. 17 years experience.

Guernsey

GUERNSEY GLASSCRAFT
(Philip A. Vivian)
Violet Lodge,
Cobo Coast Road,
Castel GY5 7HB
Tel: 01481 57417

Artist and craftsman in stained glass restoration, design and fabrication. Manufacturer of stained glass, windows, lamp shades and mirrors.

London

THE STAINED GLASS WORKSHOP
(Keith Phillips)
202a Upper Richmond Road West,
East Sheen SW14 8AN
Tel: 0181 878 5009

A specialist in stained glass windows, leaded lights, kiln fired painted panels, repairs and renovations within the domestic and ecclesiastical fields. Drawings and designs made to customer requirements. Advice and estimates free.

WOODCARVERS

London

CARVERS & GILDERS
9 Charterhouse Works,
Eltringham Street SW18
Tel: 0181 870 7047/Fax: 0181 874 0470

Restorers of fine eighteenth-century carved and gilded furniture and mirror frames. Traditional techniques and materials are used. New pieces designed and made to commission. Examples can be seen at our workshop by appointment.   M

CONSTRUCTION AND BUILDING RESTORATION

AIR CONDITIONING

Staffordshire

SOVEREIGN AIR CONDITIONING
(J. Whalley)
Altens, The Green,
Bagnell, Stoke-on-Trent ST9 9JR
Tel: 01782 503052/Fax: 01782 503457
Supply and fixing of all types of air conditioning. **M**

Surrey

AIR TIGHT SERVICES (D. Ballard)
Unit 1, Chantry Court, Plumpton Way,
Carshalton SM5 2DG
Tel: 0181 669 7111/Fax: 0181 647 2119
Established in 1984, this company can carry out any air-conditioning task, including safe removal of CFC refrigerant from redundant refrigeration. They can also cool, heat, humidify, dehumidify and extract air in order to preserve buildings, valuables, antiques etc. A free survey and quotation service is available locally.
M

BLASTING EQUIPMENT MANUFACTURERS

Lancashire

EASIBLASTER LTD
(Kevin Wildon)
11 King Street, Hindley,
Wigan WN2 3AW
Tel: 01942 523612
Easiblaster established themselves in 1985 as innovators in the blast cleaning industry. Their compact, portable machines, with the unique no damage control, are in great demand for restoration and renovation projects. Their range of blast cabinets are also fully adjustable to prevent damage from overblasting. **M**

BRICKWORK

Surrey

T. J. SHEPHERD HISTORIC BRICKWORK

**101 Moffat Road,
Thornton Heath CR7 8PZ
Tel/Fax: 0181 653 2438**

Independent Historic Brickwork Consultant: Tim Shepherd was General Foreman/Principal carpenter for Dove Bros Ltd at Hampton Court Palace 1978-1991. Running a highly skilled team, he worked on all aspects of the building, including over 70 of the famous decorated Tudor chimneys. Working independently, he won the Royal Institute of Chartered Surveyors "Craftsmanship in Building Conservation" award 1993 for his work at Hampton Court Palace, and most recently has been responsible for the accurate repair of over 200 arches at St Pancras Station. Also a qualified toolmaker, his emphasis is on practicality and precision. He offers an advisory, report writing and template manufacturing service to architects and owners of historic properties.

West Midlands

GARY BAYNHAM BRICKWORK
8 Ronald Grove, Birmingham B36 9HL
Tel: 0121 749 5995
Established in 1994, covering conservation, restoration, decorative brickwork, extensions, and garden walls. All tradesmen qualified to GNVQ Level 3. Free estimate within a 30 mile radius of Birmingham. **M**

BUILDING AND BUILDING RESTORATION

Avon

GRANGE BUILDING CONTRACTORS (SOUTH) LTD
16 Avonvale Road, Redfield,
Bristol BS5 9RL
Tel: 0117 955 0661/Fax: 0117 955 5101

Independent construction experts. **M**

Cheshire

PEAK BUILDERS (A. Rowbotham)
Sunny Bank Farm,
Buxton Road, Furness Vale,
Stockport SK12 7PH
Tel: 01663 746737

General builders and maintenance contractors covering commercial, industrial and domestic premises. A complete service to home and industry. **M**

Cornwall

ASSOCIATED CONSTRUCTION SERVICES
26 Barn Park, Lostwithiel,
Cornwall PL22 0PQ
Tel: 01208 873396/Mobile: 0860 652725

A complete building service offered. Domestic and commercial contracts welcome.

Hampshire

REL SPECIALIST CONTRACTS LTD
22 Old Milton Road, New Milton,
Hampshire BH25 6DX
Tel: 01425 629033/Fax: 01425 629040

Specialist repairs to concrete, stonework, stucco, mouldings etc. Resin injection work, brick stitching, industrial and protective coatings. Recommended contractor for major manufacturer of repair mortars and resins, working throughout southern England and the Channel Islands. **M**

Ireland - Co. Waterford

JOHN MOLONEY & SON
Ballinamona, Ardmore
Tel: 024 94286/Fax: 024 94112

Family run business established in 1977. Specialising in quality houses and high class restoration work. Top class craftsmanship guaranteed. **M**

Leicestershire

GILBERT PROJECTS LTD
90 St Mary's Road,
Market Harborough LE16 7DX
Tel: 01858 465647/Fax: 01858 433354

Family business currently managed by Martin Gilbert (the third generation of the Gilbert family involved with the construction industry). As well as contract work, a full design and build package is offered inclusive of plans, local authority approvals, grants, applications, cost planning and feasibility studies. **M**

Lincolnshire

R. C. CURTIS BUILDING CONTRACTOR
64 Lincoln Road, Ruskington,
Sleaford NG34 9AP
Tel: 01526 832815

Extensions, alterations, new homes, roofing, plus all types of ground work including patios, drainage, block paving. Experience in the laying of natural stone and competitive prices available. Free estimates and advice – 24hr service for emergency repairs. **M**

Oxfordshire

BOSHERS (CHOLSEY) LTD
Reading Road, Cholsey,
Wallingford OX10 9HN
Tel: 01491 651242

Specialist attention to Listed buildings within a radius of approximately 30 miles of Wallingford.

Staffordshire

MULTI DESIGN (Peter Baskerville)
Chartley Corner, Back Lane,
Hixon, Stafford ST18 0ND
Tel: 01889 270278
Fax: 01889 270278

A family run business established 1979. High quality renovation and refurbishment on all types of properties including domestic and commercial. Work covers from concept to completion. Free estimates. All work guaranteed. Also members of the Federation of Master Builders and National House Building Council.   **M**

Surrey

W. KNIGHT & SON
9 Howard Road, Reigate RH2 7JE
Tel: 01737 248481

Established 1909. A family firm covering extensions, alterations, renovations and maintenance of both old and new properties. All trades carried out by skilled craftsmen with personal supervision. High quality work with special attention given to reproduction of original details where required. Full design, planning, drawing service available within a 25 mile radius.   **M**

Tyne & Wear

ARMAN CONSTRUCTION LTD
(L. Cornwell)
59 Whitley Road, Whitley Bay,
Tyne & Wear NE26 2ET
Tel: 0191 251 0858
Fax: 0191 251 5707

Experts in building construction, specialising in building, design, restoration and site management.   **M**

LES SMITH
(C. & P. CONTRACTORS) LTD
57 Back Wingrove Road, Fenham,
Newcastle upon Tyne NE4 9BS
Tel: 0191 273 5538
Fax: 0191 272 2320

25 years experience in construction. Specialising in all building work; shopfitting, electrical, commercial and private work undertaken. Design and drawing service available.   **M**

Warwickshire

CLARKES BUILDING CONTRACTORS
Phillip's Field, Whichford Road,
Stourton, Shipston-on-Stour CV36 5HG
Tel: 01608 75319
Fax: 01608 75519

A team of craftsmen specialising in the renovation and extension of period properties, including stone masonry, repair and replacement of timber in oak-framed buildings, all aspects of joinery, all types of roofing and preservation work.   **M**

CARPENTERS AND JOINERS

Cumbria

ERIC J. COOK
Western View,
Skelsmergh,
Kendal LA8 9AP
Tel: 01539 823691

Established 1971. House maintenance, exterior and interior replacement doors, windows, fascia and barge boards. Roof repairs and gutters, fitted wardrobes and cupboards, floorboards, skirtings, locks, painting and wall tiling. No job too small. Private contract work undertaken within 20 mile radius of Kendal. Personal service.   **M**

Hampshire

L. DANIELS & G. ELDRIDGE
Windy Heights,
High Cross,
Froxfield,
Petersfield GU32 1EH
Tel: 01730 827472

Making and fitting of all types of wooden artefacts from all kinds of timber, man-made board, laminate, etc., constructed to customer's requirements. Specialist areas include kitchen and bedroom fitments, staircases, window frames and doors, cottage wooden door latches, and curved work. Mainly local, within 20 mile radius.   **M**

**D. J. HOLLIS & CO
(CARPENTRY CONTRACTORS) LTD**
Jays-Oak, Youngs Drive, Ash,
Aldershot GU12 6RE
Tel: 01252 20251/Fax: 01252 312050
Mobile: 0831 831215

All types of carpentry and joinery carried out, from construction of timber-framed dwellings to fully-fitted kitchens. Hand-cut roofing and all staircase work a speciality. **M**

Surrey

WARREN CARPENTRY CONTRACTORS
1 Kynaston Avenue,
Thornton Heath CR7 7BY
Tel: 0181 665 0420

All domestic and industrial woodwork undertaken. Pricework for small builders. Experience in dealing with preservation treatments. Top quality standards in 1st and 2nd fix. Everything from door and window replacements, fitted kitchens and wardrobes, structural timbers, skirting architraves, conversions and extensions. All work undertaken by experienced craftsmen.

M

Sussex (West)

W. G. DEADMAN
Willine Joinery Works, Eden Vale,
East Grinstead RH19 2JH
Tel: 01342 321840/Fax: 101342 327252

Small firm established 1952, manufacturing high class purpose-made, non-standard joinery in hardwood and softwood, for the trade and private customers. Specialising in English oak joinery, with special attention given to matching existing mouldings and details in restoration joinery. All enquiries receive personal attention. Local area, within 25 mile radius. **M**

Wiltshire

BRYAN JAMES KNOWLES
Willoughby Wind, Hindon,
Nr Salisbury SP3 6EG
Tel: 01747 820382

Master carpenter and joiner. All types of carpentry and joinery undertaken, including hip-and-valley roofs, etc. Made-to-measure joinery, i.e. doors, windows, bookcases, built-in wardrobes. Properties with preservation orders. Furniture repair and restoration. **M**

Worcestershire

DOVETAIL JOINERY
(Nigel Bird)
Unit 7, Field Barn Lane,
Cropthorne,
Evesham WR10 3LY
Tel: 01386 861123
Fax: 01386 860975

Experts in doors, windows, conservatories, patios, hardwood and softwood. Competitive prices and free quotations. Single glazing provided to customer's specification. Also suppliers of UPVC and aluminium double glazing. **M**

Yorkshire (South)

M. J. QUAY JOINERY & BUILDING
Pantiles,
Jackys Lane,
Harthill,
Sheffield S31 8XU
Tel/Fax: 01909 277 2839

All types of joinery, building and restoration work, including replacement doors, windows, kitchens, bedroom furniture. Extensions from planning to completion, industrial and office refurbishments carried out on supply and fix, or labour only basis. Estimates and further information upon request.

HIGH RISE MAINTENANCE

Nottinghamshire

CENTRAL (HIGH RISE) LTD
Central House,
Thoresby Avenue,
Sneinton NG2 3GA
Tel: 0115 9587637

Steeplejacks, concrete repairs, all high level repairs, lightning conducter installation, testing and repair. Free binocular surveys, together with reports. Nationwide coverage. **M**

ORNAMENTAL PLASTERWORK

Surrey

GEORGE JACKSON & SONS

AD 1780

Conservation &

Restoration

Specialists

Ornamental Plasterwork

•

Composition Enrichment

UNIT 19
MITCHAM INDUSTRIAL ESTATE
STREATHAM ROAD
MITCHAM CR4 2AJ
TELEPHONE 0181 648 4343
FACSIMILE 0181 640 1986

A DIVISION OF
CLARK & FENN LIMITED

REFURBISHMENTS

Yorkshire (West)

NEW IMAGE CONCEPTS LTD
Hillside House, Church Lane,
Brighouse HD6 1AT
Tel: 01484 401208/Fax: 01484 720365

Refurbishment company specialising in carrying out alterations and refurbishments within the Licensed Leisure industries. Full design and build service available, taking the project from the planning approval state (if required) to completion of the refurbishment, providing clients with the quality of service one should expect from a Guild member. **M**

ROOFING

Essex

TREVILLION ROOFING
91 Berecroft, Harlow CM20 7SD
Tel: 01279 410308/Fax: 01279 410308
Mobile: 0585 934333

Tiling, slating, peg tiling, flat roofs, sheeting, cladding, decking and lead work carried out. **M**

Hertfordshire

THE HERTFORDSHIRE ROOFING
AND RENOVATION COMPANY
32 Field Road, Oxhey WD1 4DR
Tel/Fax: 01923 250247

Specialists in restoration and repairs to historic buildings. Skilled craftsmen in masonry, joinery/carpentry, lead/copper work, brickwork, traditional crafts, wattle and daub lime plasterers. Local authority/conservation office. S.P.A.B. member. From the humble to the grand; foundations to finials; nationwide.

Kent

LEAD SHEET ASSOCIATION LTD (LSA)
St Johns Road, Tunbridge Wells TN4 9XA
Tel: 01892 513351/Fax: 01892 535028

For 70 years the Lead Sheet Association has been firmly established as the leading authority on the correct use of lead sheet in the construction industry. Its Technical Officers provide free advice and guidance by telephone or fax, on the proper design and application of milled lead sheet (manufactured to British Standard BS1178) and can even arrange visits to site, for a nominal fee.

The LSA also produces comprehensive and award winning technical publications and promotes good working practice through a wide range of training courses available to all, at its National Training Centre in Tunbridge Wells. The Centre caters for all requirements including NVQ, CPD, Health and Safety, design and application, theory and practical, accommodating everyone from the first day apprentice to the experienced craftsman.

London

C.W. PROPERTY SERVICES LTD
126 Ashleigh Road, Mortlake SW14 8PX
Tel: 0181 876 9941
Fax: 0181 878 3942

Specialists for commercial and residential properties. Slating and tiling, torch on felts, profile 'C', waterproofing membranes. Free estimates. **M**

Norwich

ANGLIA LEAD LTD
49 Barker Street, Norwich NR2 4TN
Tel: 01603 626856/619171

Anglia Lead is one of the few companies in Britain specialising in the traditional manufacture of cast lead sheet on a sand bed, for roofing purposes. The installation of lead also forms an important part of the company's work. Projects include St Paul's Cathedral, Westminster Hall, Heveningham Hall (Suffolk), Monticello (the home of Thomas Jefferson, Virginia, USA), the Octagon (Washington DC), and numerous churches, museums, and listed buildings throughout the United Kingdom. Please contact Robert Bangay or Paul Cornfield.

Nottinghamshire

J.R.S. ROOFING LTD
Common Road, Huthwaite,
Sutton-in-Ashfield NG17 2JL
Tel: 01623 558822
Fax: 01623 556695

We are specialists in roofing, with over 70 years combined experience in roofing and roofing materials. We can provide advice and help at every stage of your project. For a quality service, free advice and competitive prices, please contact Des Mellor or Ian Cobbold.

Scotland - Fife

RUSSELL ROOFING & RENOVATION
SPECIALISTS (David Russell)
14 Lochwood Park, Kingseat, Dunfermline
KY12 0UX
Tel: 01383 726528/Mobile: 0831 384146

A small, newly established and thriving business which undertakes all aspects of roofing and building work. Customers are guaranteed a high standard of work upon completion. Strip and retile or reslate a speciality. All jobs considered – distance no object. **M**

Sussex (West)

KAYCEE ROOFING & SUPPLIES
169 Junction Road,
Burgess Hill RH15 0JW
Tel: 01444 23555
Fax: 01444 235555

Private and contract roofing. Suppliers of all types of tiles and slates, including second-hand. Family run company established over 18 years. **M**

STONEMASONS/STONE CLEANING

Berkshire

A. F. JONES MASONRY CONTRACTORS
33 Bedford Road, Reading RG1 7EX
Tel: 01734 573537

Family masonry business established in 1856. Facilities available for cutting, machining and working block stone, restoration work on churches, historic buildings and new building works. Marble, granite, slate interiors. Memorials hand carved and fixed.

Gloucestershire

A. C. DAVIS
The Retreat, Aston, Ingham Road,
Kilcot, Nr Newent GL18 1NR
Tel: 01989 82651

Stonemason and architectural carver. New work, restoration and conservation. Over 20 years experience at banker work, fixing and'letter cutting, specialising in high relief stone carving. Working area 60 mile radius of Gloucester city. **M**

Hertfordshire

**GEOFFREY BYSOUTH STONE
RESTORATION**
98b High Street, Stevenage SG1 3DW
Tel/Fax: 01438 759392

Specialists in the repair and restoration of natural stonework. Experience of work on many historic buildings including: Buckingham Palace, Palace of Westminster, Tower of London and numerous churches. Can work throughout south-east England. Also cleaning, brick repairs, leadwork and roofing. **M**

Kent

ANTIAM LTD (A. J. Shields)
Acorn Business Centre, Milton Street,
Maidstone ME16 8LL
Tel: 01622 720808/Fax: 01622 720802

A professionally run company offering a high quality service including stone and brickwork fixing. Restoration and cleaning of most types of external building fabrics with staff that can draw on a minimum of 10 years experience. A friendly service providing free estimates, advice and reports without obligation. **M**

Surrey

STONEWEST LTD
Lamberts Place, St James's Road,
Croydon CR9 2HX
Tel: 0181 684 6646/Fax: 0181 684 9323

Specialists in masonry restoration and conservation, including stone, brick, terra cotta and stucco/render. Masonry renewal, in-situ restoration and surface cleaning. Contractors to both public authorities and the private sector, with extensive experience on listed buildings. BS 5750 registered. Member of The Stone Federation.

TIMBER PRESERVATION

London

ALL TIMBER INFESTATION &
CONSULTANCY SERVICES LTD
15 Baskerville Road,
Wandsworth SW18 3RJ
Tel: 0181 874 2013/Fax: 0181 874 3021

Sound, practical, technically competent advice pro-

vided on timber decay in buildings. Money is saved or spent efficiently. Our MD, C.J.D. George MA, PhD (biochemistry of decay), MSc[+distinction], (timber engineering) DIC, AIWSc, CTIS[+credit] is uniquely qualified, academically, by experience and by his past work as a site operative. **M**

Surrey

PETER COX PRESERVATION
Heritage House, 234 High Street,
Sutton SM1 1NX
Tel: 0181 661 6600
Fax: 0181 642 0677

Specialists in damp-proofing, woodworm and dry rot control, epoxy resin repairs for structural timber and remedial wall ties. Extensive experience in the repair of listed and historic buildings. BS 5750 registered. BWPDA member. A division of Peter Cox Group Ltd. 45 Branches nationwide with addresses in local directories.

DECORATING

Gloucestershire

MARTIN J. WING
2 Holt Cottage, Culkerton,
Nr Tetbury GL8 8SS
Tel: 01285 841236
Mobile: 0850 403096

Interior decorator offering an excellent service covering most aspects of decoration. All work, from a coat of paint through to more complex paperhanging, is carried out to a high standard. Cleanliness and efficiency are all part of the service, along with advising clients on colour schemes.

Hertfordshire

A. J. WHITE
34 Harwoods Road,
West Watford WD1 7RA
Tel: 01923 241685

High class painting and decorating, interior and exterior. A very high standard of work is maintained through all aspects of trade. Free estimates can be obtained upon request. Satisfaction is guaranteed.

Lancashire

BILL HOLGATE & SON
The Bungalow, 62 Littlemoor Road,
Clitheroe, Lancashire BB7 1EW
Tel: 01200 23433

Graining and marbling, sponging, stippling, dragging and rag-rolling. Specialising in graining doors and other woodwork to simulate all popular woods, oak, mahogany, walnut etc., and marbling walls, fire surrounds, bar fronts and any surface requiring this unique form of decoration. For further details and particulars of courses, please telephone.

Scotland - Strathclyde

W. P. YUILLE PAINTER/DECORATOR
6 Cowan Crescent, Ayr,
Strathclyde KA8 9QU
Tel: 01292 260596

We make nice homes beautiful: inside or outside, your home should reflect your personality. Period styles or art decor, texture and colour planning; all wallcoverings, cornices, covings, wall panels and natural wood staining, expertly applied. **M**

Wiltshire

CASTLESHORE LTD

Skilled operatives undertake commercial, industrial and domestic works. Applicators for many specialist coatings. For further details contact G. Marshall FRICS, or L. Clements.

The Yard, Grove Farmhouse,
Ashton Road, Leigh SN6 6RF
Tel: 01285 860484
Fax: 01285 862441

M

PLASTERWORK/ORNAMENTAL DECORATORS

West Midlands

ALLIED FINISHINGS LTD (CARTWRIGHTS)
94 Foxoak Street, Cradley Heath,
Warley B64 5DP
Tel: 01384 66657

Plastering contractors and architectural plaster modellers. Work undertaken within 60 mile radius of Birmingham. **M**

Yorkshire (West)

LAW's DECS
99 Victoria Road, Eccleshill,
Bradford BD2 2DQ
Tel: 01274 638855/Fax: 01274 633216   **M**

TRIMMING DYERS

London

GOLDSMITH (Trimming Dyers)
1A Albert Avenue,
off Albert Square SW8 1BX
Tel: 0171 735 9016

Established over 30 years, specialising in match dyeing, trimming for interior designers etc. **M**

FURNITURE AND FURNISHINGS

BILLIARD AND SNOOKER TABLES

Scotland - Glasgow

TUMAX SNOOKER SERVICES
(Ken McIntosh)
181 Maryhill Road, Maryhill G20 7XJ
Tel/Fax: 0141 333 9009

Scotland's premier billiard specialists for all types of tables, i.e. snooker, diners to pool tables and full size tables. Suppliers and fitters to world no. 1 Stephen Hendry. **M**

CABINET MAKERS

Bedfordshire

R. D. LEIGHTON
15 Ibbett Close, Kempston MK43 9BT
Tel: 01234 854674

A well-established cabinet maker of standard and non-standard furniture and general joinery. Also specialises in furniture restoration and French polishing. Free estimates given. **M**

Essex

J. K. THOMPSON
Chamberlains Farm,
Sporehams Lane, Danbury CM3 4AJ
Tel: 01245 227341

Cabinet making to customer's requirements, and furniture restoration. Free estimates and design service with portfolio, including home visits to local area – from Chelmsford to Southend. Bookcases, desks, tables, bars, bureaux etc. Curved work a speciality. Trade/public welcome. Traditional, modern or something completely different – the choice is yours.

Hampshire

PETER MULLINS & SONS
CABINET MAKERS
2 St Mary's Road,
Hayling Island PO11 9BY
Tel: 01705 467141/Fax: 01705 469626

Well-established family business specialising in quality furniture, handmade to an exceptionally high standard in own workshop. Designed to customer's specific requirements. All types of hardwood used. Finishes – painted to highly polished. Advice on suitable styles and design readily offered. Repairs, antique restoration and French polishing also expertly undertaken. **M**

Kent

JOHN MANSFIELD-CLARKE
420 Main Road, Westerham Hill,
Westerham TN16 2HP
Tel: 01959 573857

Designer and cabinet maker. Hand-made fitted furniture – bookcases, wardrobes, tables etc. Full architectural service for superb kitchens in a variety of hardwoods. Also a high quality repair and restoration service, to antique furniture. **M**

Leicestershire

BRUCE ATTENBOROUGH
26 Kings Lane, South Croxton LE7 3RE
Tel: 01664 840542

Handmade furniture crafted in the traditional manner. Custom-made items include bookcases, library steps, tables, chairs, tantalus, free-standing cupboards and speciality pieces. Mostly in solid hardwoods. Also innovative garden furniture including benches, obelisk and versaille tubs, and dolls' houses for both children and collectors, in various period styles **M**

London

MAX E. OTT LTD
1a Southcote Road,
Tufnell Park N19 5BJ
Tel: 0171 607 1384/Fax: 0171 607 3506

Small firm of cabinet makers experienced in furniture and joinery manufacture to both trade and private requirements. Our work is mainly 'one-offs' to our own or customers' designs, both modern and traditional. Display and exhibition work, and shopfitting complete the range of work we are capable of undertaking. **M**

Middlesex

J. B. L. FURNITURE - INTERIORS & DESIGN
The Coachyard, 61 Fern Grove,
Feltham TW14 9AY
Tel: 0181 890 3456/Fax: 0181 890 3455

Cabinetmaker and furniture designer, taking on special commissioned work, but principally designing and making custom furniture and fitments to fit and blend with existing decor. Any style, from early English to ultra-modern, in any wood, including brass and veneer inlay work. **M**

Yorkshire (South)

COUNTRY DREAM AND OPTIONS
(D. Coultas)
The Farmhouse, Ingbirchworth,
Penistone, Sheffield S30 6GF
Tel: 01226 766027

Kitchen units genuinely hand-made by skilled craftsmen using traditional methods and skills. Each cabinet is made to the unique requirements of the individual client. We also supply appliances by all leading manufacturers. A prompt, professional, friendly service, with no obligation; advice and assistance provided. A full and inclusive design service available. **M**

CANE AND RUSH

Hampshire

JOHN HAYWARD
(John and Christine Hayward)
Cane and Woodcraft Centre,
57 High Street, Beaulieu SO42 7YA
Tel: 01590 612211

Restoration of antique and modern furniture with traditional, bergère, close-caned, pre-woven cane, rush and seagrass seats, etc. Commission for stately homes, museums and the antique trade are frequently undertaken. Catalogue of new stools, children's chairs and headboards on request. New work, traditionally made, undertaken. **M**

Kent

ALGAR'S CHAIR CANING SERVICE
(Janice Algar)
22 Orchard Road,
Swanscombe DA10 0AE
Tel: 01322 383982

Established 1984, this family-owned chair caning and rush seaters service, has a team of highly-skilled restorers. It specialises in repairing antique and modern furniture in cane, dutch rush or somic twine. We specialise in sunray, circular, blind or through cane. Free estimates. Deliveries and collections can be arranged. **M**

London

P. J. AVERSON-MAUNDER
73 Queen Anne's Grove, Ealing W5 3XP
Tel: 0181 567 6586

Rush and cane reseating of antique and modern furniture to high standards of workmanship. Quality natural materials are used. Danish cord, pre-woven cane and seagrass seating undertaken. Work undertaken within a 10 mile radius of London. Estimates free if work can be examined, except for insurance claims. **M**

Sussex (East)

PAUL BOULTON
Burwash Post Office TN19 7EP
Tel: 01435 882201

Specialist in all types of cane furniture repairs i.e. blind, double-sided and French caning, bergère, medallion, sunburst, wicker and pre-woven cane (office chairs etc). Also Danish cord, Lloyd Loom, rush fibre, seagrass. Discounts available on second and subsequent chairs. Collection and delivery service free of charge in Kent/Sussex. **M**

FLOORING

Essex

CARPET MATTERS OF SOUTHCHURCH
685 Southchurch Road,
Southend-on-Sea SS1 2PW
Tel: 01702 616324

Friendly, reliable service with no hidden extras. Mobile home service. Free fitting, expert advice and estimates. Refits and restretching. All makes of carpets and vinyl. Screeding and hardboarding. 15 years experience. **M**

CHARTER INTERIOR CONTRACTS LTD
Unit 3, Bankside Park,
28 Thames Road, Barking IG11 0HZ
Tel: 0181 594 0220/Fax: 0181 594 0757

Carpets and blinds - a complete service from survey to manufacture, installation and maintenance. Carpets and floorcovering - commercial carpet flooring and safety floor installations carried out daily. **M**

PETER ALEXANDER CARPETS
69 Ongar Road, Brentwood
Tel: 01277 220100

Peter Alexander Carpets was formed in 1984 by Peter Alexander and Ted Shuttleworth, quickly joined by Clive Palmer to create a formidable team of professional carpet people. The Company has traded successfully and progressively in the domestic and showhome markets by offering service and quality at competitive prices **M**

Hampshire

CARPETEC (J.M. Motherwell)
83 Satchell Lane, Hamble-le-Rice,
Southampton SO31 4HH
Tel: 01703 456792/783783

All aspects of carpet and vinyl fitting undertaken, including refits, repairs and restretching. Quality carpets and vinyls supplied at the very best prices. Home selection service. Distance no object. Telephone for prompt attention. **M**

Kent

R. D. B. SQUIRES & CO
10 Upperton Road,
Sidcup DA14 6AT
Tel: 0181 300 7377/Fax: 0181 309 5898

Established over 25 years. Carpet fitting/planning service, site cleaning and stain-proofing. Domestic and contract work. Materials supplied and samples brought to your home or premises. Areas covered: south-east London and north-west Kent. **M**

London

ANGLO PERSIAN CARPET CO
South Kensington
Station Arcade SW7 2NA
Tel: 0171 589 5457/Fax: 0171 589 2592

Specialist oriental carpet restorers and cleaners. **M**

Nottinghamshire

CASTLE CARPETS
63-67 Main Street,
Shirebrook,
Nr Mansfield NG20 8AN
Tel: 01623 743619/Fax: 01623 747616

Established since 1960. Quality at sensible prices. All top manufactured carpets in store.

Excellent advice. Top quality fitting service. Before you buy, give us a try. Ask for Bill, Frank or Kevin.

Surrey

BELLE DESIGNS LTD
(S. Psaila)
15 Belle Street,
Reigate RH2 7AD
Tel/Fax: 01737 225536 **M**

Tyne & Wear

HOUGHTON CARPET CENTRE
(Bob Wood)
33 Newbottle Street,
Houghton-le-Spring DH4 4AP
Tel: 0191 584 6657

Expert fitting service, free estimates and delivery service. All carpets and vinyls at competitive prices. **M**

Yorkshire (North)

DENNIS YORKE
24 The Village,
Haxby YO3 3HT
Tel: 01904 769689/Fax: 01904 750053

The finest collection of fitted carpets. Their fitters are renowned craftsmen. Expertise is second to none. The largest selection of oriental rugs and carpets outside the London area and over 2000 in stock at all times. **M**

Yorkshire (South)

THE KITCHEN FLOOR LTD
919 Abbeydale Road,
Sheffield S7 2BJ
Tel: 0114 2500441

Wood, vinyl floors, Amtico tiles, carpet tiles, cork tiles, linoleum sheet and tiles. Contract and domestic work. Fitting and estimating service. Patterns to see at home: over 2000 to choose from, including wood, cork, ceramic and slate tiles. Expert repair service. **M**

FURNITURE RESTORATION

Dorset

TONY MEADLEY
6 Thistlegate Cottages, Axminster Road,
Charmouth, Bridport DT6 6BU
Tel: 01297 560335

A small, friendly family business specialising in the repair and restoration of antique furniture. All aspects of restoration are covered, including structural repair, French polishing, inlaying and veneering, carving, cane and rushwork, and seat upholstery. All work is sympathetically executed. Free quotations and home visits provided. **M**

Hampshire

FINE FURNITURE BY M. B. CLUBLEY
(M.B. Clubley)
Unit 007, Victory Business Centre,
Somers Road, North Portsmouth PO1 1PJ
Tel: 01705 826201

For the past 35 years, making, caring for and restoring furniture to a very high standard. **M**

London

S. & H. JEWELL LTD
26 Parker Street WC2B 5PH
Tel: 0171 405 8520
All aspects of furniture restoration, repair, polishing, relining of tops, upholstery, carving, gilding, glass tops and door panes. Furniture custom-made. **M**

Scotland
East Lothian

MYRESIDE SCHOOL OF ANTIQUE FURNITURE RESTORATION
(Principal: Anselm Fraser)
Myreside Grange, Gifford,
East Lothian EH41 4JA
Tel: 01620 810680/Fax: 01620 826285
The Myreside School houses a commercial antique furniture restoration business undertaking such restoration skills as gilding, marquetry, boulle work, French polishing, gesso mouldings, wood carving and turning. From spacious workshops they also produce free-standing kitchen furniture made to order incorporating the traditional joints and solidity of original farmhouse furniture.

Fife

ALASTAIR GUNN
Dunimarle Castle, Culross,
Dunfermline KY12 8JN
Tel: 01383 881515
Restoration of antique furniture, veneering, woodcarving, woodturning, boulle work, marquetry, brass inlays, gilding, gesso mouldings, French polishing, simple upholstery, structural repairs. **M**

Suffolk

PETER JOHNSTON & COMPANY
(Peter Johnston)
The Homestead, Horham, Eye IP21 5DX
Tel: 01379 384654
The business was established in 1972, undertaking high quality repairs and maintenance to period houses. More specialised carpentry and furniture making are also available, together with antique furniture repairs. A design and advice service are offered, including estimates.

Surrey

REMBRANT FURNITURE RESTORERS
(Gerald F. Leonard)
72 Byron Avenue, Motspur Park KT3 6EY
Tel/Fax: 0181 949 4611
Mobile: 0956 273480
Family business of antique and modern furniture restorers, specialising in small repairs. Highly-skilled craftsmen, undertake French polishing, reupholstery, recaning, leather desk tops, wood and veneer repairs for private and trade clients. Rembrant's motto, 'our reputation starts with our finish', speaks for itself. A very personal service.

MICHAEL SCHRYVER ANTIQUES LTD
The Granary, 10 North Street,
Dorking RH4 1DN
Tel: 01306 881110
Fax: 01306 876168
Restorers of fine period furniture; highest quality craftsmanship; cabinet making; polishing; metalwork; period and modern upholstery. Deliveries weekly to London and a radius of 50 miles around Dorking. **M**

Tyne & Wear

THE NORTHERN TRAINING TRUST LIMITED
7 Tilley Road,
Crowther Industrial Estate,
Washington NE38 0AE
Tel: 0191 417 9696/Fax: 0191 415 0955
Manufacturers of bespoke and standard furniture. Also reupholster all items of furniture. Specialising in restoration work, polishing and finishing. Garden huts and furniture made to order. Registered trainees in furniture craft skills.

Yorkshire (North)

ACORN INDUSTRIES
(G. J. Grainger & Son)
Brandsby, York YO6 4RG
Tel: 01347 888217
Furniture made in most hardwoods to a high standard and in many designs. All the pieces made have an acorn carved on them, which is our trademark and the guarantee of a well-made article. Restorations and French polishing also carried out.

Yorkshire (West)

J. H. COOPER & SON (ILKLEY) LTD
COOPERS OF ILKLEY
33-35 Church Street,
Ilkley LS29 9DR
Tel: 01943 608020

Principal: Charles Cooper

A long-established family business, offering a comprehensive restoration service of antique furniture, from repairing, polishing and upholstering to cabinet making. Prices include collection and delivery. Also specialise in the making of individual pieces to customer's specifications, from extra chairs to make up dining sets, to wing book cases etc.

MUSICAL INSTRUMENTS

Oxfordshire

EARLY KEYBOARD AGENCY
Heyford Galleries,
High Street,
Upper Heyford,
Bicester OX6 3LE
Tel: 01869 232282

More than 30 years experience in the restoration, manufacture and maintenance of early keyboard instruments – harpsichords, etc. We restore both antique and modern instruments to the highest standards in our workshops. Our clientele includes well-known players, orchestras, schools, colleges and universities, as well as private individuals.

SOFT FURNISHINGS

West Midlands

DEE MUIR CURTAINS
351 High Street,
Harborne,
Birmingham B17 9QN
Tel: 0121 428589   M

GARDEN AND LANDSCAPE SERVICES

Essex

PINEWOOD LANDSCAPES
(M. Andrews)
10 Devises House, Montgomery Crescent,
Harold Hill RM3 7UP
Tel: 0181 590 0545

Established 1984. Landscapes and driveway specialists. Services include block paving, pattern imprinted concrete, crazy paving, slab patios, turfing, fencing, walling. A display of pattern imprinted concrete can be seen at Sungate Nursery, Collier Row Road, Romford. For free estimate and advice telephone 0181 590 0545.

M

Sussex(East)

P. J. TIPPING
Europlants, Streetfield Farm,
Cade Street, Heathfield TN21 9BS
Tel: 0143 866277
Fax: 01435 867054

Europlants, established 1986, has three main areas of service. Importing tropical plants direct from European market to local garden centres, also for our own usage within our Interior/Exterior Landscaping divisions, which offer a complete service, from design of planting schedules, to installation and maintenance, if required.

Scotland - Fife

BRIAN PURVIS LANDSCAPES
(Brian Purvis)
3 Hays Road, Gauldry,
Newport-on-Tay DD6 8SJ
Tel: 01382 330 587/553 429

We undertake designing, hard and soft landscape layouts, seasonal maintenance, rotovating, ground preparation and disabled gardens. Also lawn turfing, seeding, grass cutting and related grass maintenance. We welcome domestic and small commercial contracts. All work undertaken by qualified, experienced and caring professionals. All enquiries welcome, and estimates are free.   M

Somerset

ANDREW TABOR LANDSCAPING
Meleor, Sparkford,
Yeovil BA22 7JF
Tel: 01935 850594

All garden design and landscaping services carried out from reorganisation of plants and herbaceous borders to laying lawns, construction of drives, paths, patios, tree surgery and pruning. Design and construction of ponds, stonewalling and fencing. Quotations or piecework available. All work completed quickly and efficiently. **M**

Surrey

TRIFFID LANDSCAPES
(James Bligh)
Temple Pool,
Dockenfield,
Farnham GU10 4HP
Tel: 01252 792734

RHS qualified. Pride is taken in extensive range of garden services, including all aspects of garden design and construction. Also undertake specialised work in tree surgery, water features and fencing. Free advice and a professional reliable service seven days a week. **M**

TREE SURGEONS

Northumberland

**COLIN WHITE TREE SURGERY
AND FORESTRY CONTRACTOR**
The Manor House,
Colwell,
Hexham NE46 4TL
Tel: 01434 681598
Fax: 01434 681598

Forestry, tree surgery, woodland management, estate and landscape maintenance. Stump and brushwood chipping service. **M**

HOME IMPROVEMENTS AND PROPERTY MAINTENANCE

CHIMNEYS

Suffolk

CICO CHIMNEY LININGS LTD
Westleton, Saxmundham IP17 3BS
Tel: 01728 648 608/Fax: 01728 648 428

Advisory and installation service covering chimney problems from 20 branches throughout the country. CICO cast-in-situ process, lining and installation, is approved by the British Board of Agrément. No joints to work loose and leak, and being non-metallic is not subject to corrosion. Rebuilt from the inside and suitable for all fuels.

CONSERVATORIES

Worcestershire

STATUS CONSERVATORIES
(Alan Karlsson Jones)
Little Heath Garden Centre, Lickey End,
Bromsgrove B60 1HY
Tel/Fax: 01527 577699

A family business with over 23 years experience. A total service from concept to completion. Design and instal conservatories in any size, shape and material, plus floor, electrics, fans and furnishings. Free estimates and nationwide installation. **M**

DRAUGHT PROOFING

West Midlands

JOATRAD SERVICES LTD
3rd Floor, Kelvin Way,
West Bromwich B70 7JW
Tel: 0121 553 1075/Fax: 0121 553 0102

Draught proofing, insulation work carried out. Plus garden landscaping. **M**

FIREPLACES

Surrey

WAKEFORD FIREPLACES
154 Send Road,
Send, Woking GU23 7EZ
Tel: 01483 223900
Fax: 01483 225363

Fireplaces, fires, stoves and chimneys are a speciality. Experience in assisting the customer to make the right choice for the home, whether it is replacing the existing fire, the whole fireplace, lining the chimney or solving a problem. Members of the NFA, CORGI and British Coal approved. **M**

Yorkshire (West)

SANDAL FIRES & FIRE SURROUNDS
(B Axelsen)
15 Belle Vue Road, Sandal,
Wakefield WF1 5NF
Tel: 01924 2592114

Retailers and suppliers of fireplaces – gas, electric and solid fuel fires. Marble, tiles and cast iron interiors available. Custom service, including size, colour etc, provided by specialists. **M**

FITTED FURNITURE

Essex

THOMPSON INTERIORS
(Roy Thompson)
Unit 15,
Redif Industrial Estate,
Wantz Road,
Dagenham RM10 8PS
Tel: 0181 595 7243

Design, manufacture and installation of kitchens, bathrooms, bedrooms and lounge furniture, including all building services for the private domestic clients. Also design, build and install executive suites, boardrooms, presentation theatres, reception areas, including provision of all associated services for the commercial customer. **M**

KITCHENS

Lincolnshire

ECONOMY KITCHENS
Unit C, The Malt House,
Harrowby Road, Grantham
Tel: 01476 66883

High quality kitchens at low cost. Also available – appliances, sinks, worktops, etc. Fitting can be arranged.

KITCHEN GALLERY
3 Dorridge Square, Dorridge,
Nr Solihull, West Midlands B93 8HN
Tel: 01564 773389

We are specialists in the complete fitted kitchen and main dealers for some of the world's finest kitchen equipment, including Siematic and a British hand-made kitchen; Neff, De-Dietrich and Gaggenau appliances; Corian work surfaces and Amtico floors. Many years experience ensures the finest design and the most expert installation. **M**

LOCKSMITHS

London

V. & P. FOX
23 Cecil Court, St Martins Lane WC2
Tel: 0171 836 2902

All types of keys cut, locks fitted, safes opened and repaired (wall and floor safes). Telephone entry systems installed. **M**

MAINTENANCE

Devon

N. A. STANDRING & CO
(N. A. Standring)
Sidbury Mill, Sidbury,
Sidmouth EX10 0RE
Tel: 01395 597221

Restoration, maintenance and alterations, including kitchens and bathrooms designed and fitted. Decorating, carpentry, joinery, plumbing and general building. Many years experience of working on cob stone and character properties, but equally happy to undertake works on newer properties. **M**

Wales - Glamorgan (South)

GROSVENOR PROPERTY MAINTENANCE (T. George)
32 Churchill Way, Cardiff CF1 4DZ
Tel: 01222 225205/Fax: 01222 344067

A unique personal service offering total property maintenance. Building work: property refurbishment, extensions, conservatories and general repairs. Services: plumbing, electrical, gas and heating engineering, carpentry, decorating, landscaping and the supply of domestic appliances. General maintenance: maintaining electrical equipment, cleaning, gardening and pest control. Emergency Services (24 hour): locksmith, glazier, plumber, electrician. **M**

STAINED GLASS

Northamptonshire

RRC STAINED GLASS COMPANY
(R.R. Clark)
Orchard Cottage,
39 Fulwell Road, Westbury,
Brackley NN13 5PR
Tel: 01280 700876

Ours is a small and reliable business specialising in the restoration of leaded lights and stained glass windows, as well as refurbishing metal and wooden frames. Commissions for new designs are happily undertaken. Whether your property is old or new, give us a ring: we'll be pleased to help. **M**

WINDOWS

Gwent

VIEWPOINT WINDOWS LTD
Units 18/20, Mill Street,
Abergavenny NP7 5HE
Tel: 01873 856806/Fax: 01873 854183

This old, established company manufactures and installs high quality UPVC windows, doors and conservatories for the building industry and the domestic replacement market. Contracts range in size from individual properties to major new building constructions. A free, highly competitive survey and quotation service is available on request. **M**

Hertfordshire

J.W.F. WINDOWS
(J. W. Fellowes)
2 Mount Close,
Hemel Hempstead HP1 2BD
Tel: 01442 256156

Window installation and joinery, home maintenance, UPVC cladding and guttering. **M**

HOUSEHOLD UTILITIES AND SERVICES

CLEANING

Berkshire

HALES SERVICES
60 Tippits Mead,
Bracknell RG12 1FH
Tel: 01344 411293

Established 1968. Office and factory cleaning, windows, floor treatments, carpets, builders and initial cleans. Ground and property maintenance. Office removals. Fully insured. High standards, competitive rates. **M**

Hampshire

SQUARE 1 CLEANING SERVICES
(Patrick Templeman)
Chappets, West Meon,
Petersfield GU32 1NB
Tel: 0800 525549
Fax: 01730 829799

All types of cleaning for the home or business undertaken with care and pride – Hampshire and surrounding counties. Also specialist cleaners for carpets, curtains, upholstery and fire or flood damage restoration. Call on freephone number. **M**

ELECTRICAL

Derbyshire

LOGIC ELECTRICAL ENGINEERS LTD
Godfrey Street,
Market Place,
Heanor DE75 7GD
Tel: 01773 769680   M

Essex

MURLEY ELECTRICAL LTD
2 Rural Close,
Hornchurch RM11 1FH
Tel: 01708 479130
Fax: 01708 440612

Specialists in commercial and industrial electrical installations and can provide a full design package using computer aided design and drawing facilities. Full details are available on request.   M

Herefordshire

D. A. ELECTRICAL AND SOFTWARE SOLUTIONS
The Laburnums,
32a High Street,
Kington HR5 3BJ
Tel: 01544 230254

Installation of specialist electrical/audio equipment. Power light and sound. Dolby, Prologic, Satellite, Multiroom. Audio video, hi-fi, retail from Harmon, JBL, Jamo Alphason, Pace, Nokia, Philips, Yamaha. Software all formats, LP, CD, CDI, Corom, Video, etc.

CRAIG PADFIELD ELECTRICAL LTD
Unit 3, Old Wharfe Industrial Estate,
Dymolk Road,
Ledbury HR8 2HS
Tel: 01531 631763   M

Leicestershire

F. A. WINDER & CO LTD
14 Shaftesbury Road,
Leicester LE3 0QN
Tel: 0116 247 0178/Mobile: 0585 788590

Domestic and industrial installations carried out. N.I.C.E.I.C. approved contractors.   M

Lincolnshire

CLARKE ELECTRICAL (Dave Clarke)
Church House,
Horsington,
Lincoln LN3 5EX
Tel: 01526 388235

All industrial commercial and domestic electrical work undertaken. Also domestic intruder alarm systems. Domestic appliance repairs, portable electric tool repairs, and portable appliance testing. Computer printed certificates given. 28 years experience. All work complies to current regulations.   M

Nottinghamshire

DEREK GEEVES ELECTRICAL CONTRACTOR
39 Terrace Lane,
Pleasley,
Mansfield NG19 7PY
Tel: 01623 810526

Industrial and commercial installations. Can design, manufacture and install motor control panels and ventilation systems, including equipment for hazardous environments. Supply and install gas, heat, flame and smoke detection systems designed for your individual requirements. For prompt nationwide service and quotations telephone the above number – 24 hour answerphone.   M

Surrey

CROYDON POWER & LIGHT LTD
162-164 Selsdon Road,
South Croydon CR2 6PJ
Tel: 0181 681 3275
Fax: 0181 686 3930

Electrical contractors and alarm installations undertaken.   M

Tyne & Wear

A. K. ELECTRICAL (A. Kime)
434 Grace Street, Byker,
Newcastle Upon Tyne NE6 2RQ
Tel: 0191 276 6361
Fax: 0191 224 2559

Commercial and domestic installations, intruder alarms, showers, rewires, security lighting, maintenance contracts. Free estimates.   M

Yorkshire (South)

HARDY PROPERTY SERVICES (H.P.S)

Electrical and mechanical contractors. Lighting sockets, rewires all carried out to I.E.E. regulations (16th edition). Burglar and fire alarms, plumbing/heating, boiler and gas appliance servicing, fitting and repairs. All work fully guaranteed. Free quotes and advice – 24 hour call out. ACOP, CORGI registered.

8 Helmsley Avenue, Halfway, Sheffield S19 5SR Tel: 0114 2477156 Mobile: 0831 368121

M

PLUMBING & HEATING

Essex

B.H.S.D.
17-18 Industrial Centre,
Brook Road,
Rayleigh SS6 7XL
Tel: 01268 743727

Plumbing and heating installation and servicing undertaken. **M**

Nottinghamshire

K. & M. PLUMBING &
PLASTERING REPAIRS
28 Boy Lane,
Edwinstone,
Mansfield NG21 9RA
Tel: 01623 825008

Central heating, bathrooms, kitchens etc. General plumbing and plastering carried out. **M**

REMOVALS

Essex

W. NORTON & SONS
(Donald W.C. Norton)
Rokeby, Upper Avenue,
Bowers, Gifford,
Basildon SS13 2LR
Tel: 01268 726639

Established over 60 years. Removal of household and office furniture. Boxes supplied free. Local and long distance. Estimates free and special rates for OAP's. Carpets lifted and refitted if required. **M**

SECURITY

Kent

WEALDEN SECURITY CENTRE
2 The Fairings,
Ashford Road,
Tenterden TN30 6QX
Tel/Fax: 01580 766796

We specialise in safes, burglary repairs and security fitting of Chubb, Yale, Era, Ingersoll door and window locks, padlocks and grilles. Call and see our wide range of security products including: alarms, lighting, fire extinguishers, C.C.T.V., marking, vehicle security, access control. Full key cutting facility. Proprietor, Richard Birch, has 30 years experience in domestic and international security. **M**

TELECOMMUNICATIONS

Kent

SWIFTNET
(Graham F. Bennett)
28 Headcorn Road,
Platts Heath,
Lenham ME17 2NH
Tel: 01622 850264

Business and domestic telephone systems installed by ex-BT engineers.

LEISURE

GOLF

Isle of Wight

1066 GOLF (Mr N. R. Bartlett)
96 Pellhurst Road, Ryde PO33 3DR
Tel: 01983 562768

Professional Clubmakers Society's designated Class A clubmaker specialising in made-to-measure sets and single clubs. Comprehensive club repair service from regripping, rebuilding and refurbishment, to customising existing clubs by adjustment and alteration to fit golfer's natural swing pattern. **M**

Leicestershire

RANGE PRODUCTS
(GOLF WORKSHOP)

Manufacturers of golf course and putting green equipment. Professional golf club repairers: regripping, rebinding, reshafting and refurbishing.

**35 Grosvenor Crescent,
Oadby, Leicester LE2 5FP**

**Tel: 0116 271 4526
Fax: 0116 271 0477**
M

PHOTOGRAPHIC

Hertfordshire

T. J. KENYON (STEVENAGE) LTD
Bessemer Drive,
Stevenage SG1 2DL
Tel: 01438 720888/Fax: 01438 743551

Specialists in the repair of most makes of photographic cameras, video camcorders, VCR's, photo CD players and accessories. Warranty approved by Kodak, Samsung, J.V.C., Gossen and Simda. National approved repairer for Kodak Carousel and Extapro projectors and Kodak photo CD players. Photoprocessing and photo retail. **M**

SAILING

Kent

ELLIOTT SAILMAKERS
College Road,
Chatham Historic Dockyard,
Chatham ME4 4TE
Tel: 01634 408160

Manufacturers of traditional and modern sails, sprayhoods, canopies, cockpit covers, sail covers, lettered dodgers, laying up covers, screens, tarpaulins, upholstery, sail bags, duffle bags, halyard bags and anything to suit personal needs. All year round sail and cover valeting. Full overhaul and repair service. **M**

METALWORKERS

ENGRAVING

Hampshire

B.H.R. PRECISION ENGRAVING
(B. Robinson)
209/211 Victory Business Centre,
Somers Road, North Portsmouth PO1 1PJ
Tel: 01705 816613

Engravers to industry. Specialist engraving on moulds and mimic diagrams. Reverse engraved perspex coloured to requirements, traffolyte, anodised aluminium, brass or customer's free issue. Signs, nameplates, electronic labels. Our specialist team can give professional advice on all engraving problems. **M**

Sussex (East)

P. & S. ENGRAVING
38a Norway Street, Portslade BN4 1AE
Tel: 01273 424801

All machine engraving, from labels to clock dials. Specialising in manufacturing finishing tools for bookbinders and leather workers for gold embossing onto leather and foil printing. Tools supplied: handle letters, gouges, brass type, pallets, hand tools, fillets and decorative wheels – deeply cut to produce sharp impressions even on soft leathers. **M**

METAL POLISHERS
West Midlands

R. C. BERESFORD LTD
48 St Georges Street, Hockley,
Birmingham B19 3QU
Tel: 0121 236 8455

Hand metal spinning, light press work and polishing available. **M**

PAINT FINISHERS
Hertfordshire

CONQUEROR INDUSTRIES LTD
Royston Trading Estate, Units 3 & 4,
South Close,
Royston SG8 5HA
Tel: 01763 249535

Industrial finishing, plastic coat, shot-blasting and stove enamelling undertaken. **M**

Middlesex

TECKFON SPRAY COATINGS
(John Holmes)
Shepperton Studio Centre,
Shepperton
Tel: 01932 563237/Fax: 01932 572205

Teckfon have been applying paint finishes for 30 years. Various paint finishes i.e. enamels, cellulose, two-packs etc., can be applied in any texture and colour. Also car bodywork repairs from a small dent to a total repaint can be undertaken. Car service and repairs, MOT's also carried out. **M**

SIGNMAKERS
Cheshire

K. B. L. ENGRAVING SERVICE LTD
127 Albert Road,
Widnes WA8 6LB
Tel: 0151 420 3675/Fax: 0151 495 1627

Industrial and architectural engravers. Signs, labels, nameplates, mimics, fascias and trophies.

TROPHIES

RELIABLE STAMPING LTD
Rear of 16 Tenby Street,
North Birmingham B1 3EN
Tel: 0121 236 0184/Fax: 0121 233 3551

Established 1968. Manufacturers of badges, medals and items allied to this trade. Dies made to your requirements. High quality competitive prices. Personal service. Plating facility available, brochure on request. **M**

TRADITIONAL AND RURAL CRAFTS

BLACKSMITHS
Hampshire

ALL KINDS OF IRON WORK
(Peter Clutterbuck)
Rear of 38 Osborne Road,
Southsea, Portsmouth
Tel: 01705 753562

All kinds of ironwork, forge work, firebaskets, spiral stairs, balustrades; reproduction work, renovations, gates, railings, security/decorative panels, screens, repairs. You name it, we can do it.

Sussex (East)

G. W. DAY & CO
East Chiltington Forge,
Highbridge Lane,
Nr Lewes BN7 3QY
Tel/Fax: 01273 890398

Established 1950, these traditional blacksmiths specialise in quality wrought ironwork and restoration of ironwork and architectural ironmongery. Restoration work has been carried out at many listed properties and castles. New entrance gates are a feature of their work, a recent example being a pair of entrance gates at RAF Northolt. **M**

𝕲. 𝖂. 𝕯𝖆𝖞 & 𝕮𝖔.
𝕭𝖑𝖆𝖈𝖐𝖘𝖒𝖎𝖙𝖍𝖘

G. W. Day & Co. are traditional Blacksmiths and have produced quality ironwork at their East Chiltington forge since 1950.
All work is made to order, either to our design or to customer's specification, and covers a full range including gates, railings, balcony balustrading, staircases, grilles, rose arches, rose arbours, chandeliers, metal furniture and curtain poles.
Restoration to ironwork (wrought or cast) and architectural ironmongery.

**East Chiltington Forge,
Highbridge Lane, Near Lewes,
East Sussex BN7 3QY.
Telephone and Fax:
01273 890398**

SADDLERY
Kent

MARGARET NEWING
37 Mereworth Road,
Tunbridge Wells TN4 9PL
Tel: 01892 533382
Recently qualified to City and Guilds standard in leather goods and saddlery. Commissions accepted for the manufacture of traditional hand-stitched leather cases, and hunting kit bags, saddlery and harnesses. Repair work for these items also undertaken.   **M**

WALKING STICKS
Berkshire

WOODLAND CRAFTS
(John E. Kirkby)
2 Holt Cottages,
Ashford Hill,
Nr Newbury RG15 8BH
Tel: 01734 815635
Finest quality, hand-crafted walking, rambling and hiking sticks, all made from well-seasoned hazel shafts and deer horn, and made to specification. Craftsmanship is high, but prices are low. Repairs undertaken. No order too small or too big. Callers by appointment.   **M**

WOODTURNERS
Staffordshire

BURTON WOOD TURNERY
(M. H. Cherry)
Wetmore Road,
Burton-on-Trent DE14 1QN
Tel: 01283 563455/Fax: 01283 511526
Established in 1897 and registered to ISO9002. A personal and professional service is offered and 'one offs' or multi production runs are provided. Particular pride is taken in restoration turnings and architectural work. Free estimates and nationwide delivery service provided.   **M**

PROFESSIONAL SERVICES

ARCHITECTURAL/ INTERIOR DESIGN

Hertfordshire

GRAHAM D. MARTIN FCSD
55 Uxbridge Road,
Rickmansworth WD3 2DQ
Tel: 01923 776799

Chartered designer offers assistance with architectural and interior projects, whether domestic, commercial or ecclesiastical. Expertise with listed buildings and other old properties. Advice, design, local authority approvals, tenders and contract administration for repairs, alterations, extensions, interiors, furnishings.
M

FURNISHING

Harman Fox
Contract Furnishing Consultants and Services

Established 1990, this Partnership offers a full Consultation, Specifying and supply service in relation to hard and soft Furnishings and Floor Coverings. With 10 years Joinery experience in Shopfitting and 23 years Technical grounding in HM Government's Furnishings department we are able to deal with all aspects of Contract Furnishings.

**450 Walsall Road,
Perry Barr,
Birmingham B42 2LX
Tel: 0212 356
Fax: 0121 356 9800**

LANDSCAPE

Sussex (East)

A. du GARD PASLEY FLI FSGD
3 The Homestead,
Corseley Road,
Groombridge TN3 9RN
Tel: 01892 864548

Landscape architect, consultant and lecturer. For the past 25 years specialising in the restoration of historic gardens and estates, to achieve an authentic effect with reduced labour. New gardens tailored to the wishes of the owner and the character of the surroundings. Lectures and garden visits arranged.   **M**

QUANTITY SURVEYORS

Scotland - Edinburgh

GIBSON & SIMPSON SURVEYORS LTD
(Robert Moyes and Martin Jarvie)
Hailes House, 32 Hailes Avenue
EH13 0LZ
Tel: 0131 441 6655/Fax: 0131 441 6601

Founded in 1890. We provide quantity surveying and cost consultancy services throughout Scotland. The team has wide experience of restoration, refurbishment, repair and alteration to property, including several well-known Scottish historic buildings. Other services include building surveying, dilapidations, and fire insurance valuations. An efficient, caring service, at a sensible, competitive price.

Surrey

DAVID MASKELL ASSOCIATES
(David Maskell)
Elmsleigh School House,
3 The Fairfield,
Farnham GU9 8AH
Tel: 01252 710958/Fax: 01252 737152

David Maskell Associates are a small Surrey-based practice with a growing reputation in the field of repair, alteration and conservation of listed buildings. Applications for grant aid are prepared and cost advice given on all types of projects, together with procurement methods for building work and maintenance programmes.

SPECIALIST RETAILERS

ARTIST'S MATERIALS

Oxfordshire

CRAFTSMEN'S GALLERY
1 Market Street ,Woodstock,
Oxford OX20 1SU
Tel: 01993 811995

Specialises in work by British artists and craftsmen, in oils, watercolours, ceramics, wood etc. Well-stocked artists' materials section including the main producers (Daler-Rowney, Winsor & Newton, Caran D'Ache etc). Items not in stock can be obtained at short notice. Complete picture framing service.

BEDDING

Staffordshire

BRIDGTOWN BED CENTRE
22 Broad Street, Bridgtown,
Cannock WS11 3DA
Tel: 01543 572828

Largest selection of top quality brands of beds and sofa beds. A comprehensive choice of bedroom furniture and traditional bed covers, eiderdowns etc. Individual beds for individual people. A made-to-measure service for difficult and unusual sizes in beds and bed linen.

M

CARAVAN

Scotland - Fife

WALLACE CARAVANS (KIRKCALDY)
(David Wallace)
Thornton Road,
Kirkcaldy KY1 3NW
Tel: 01592 774265/Fax: 01592 630607

Luxury touring caravan sales and hires. Stockists for Witter towbars. Specialist fitting service available. Five star, NCC, RAC and Caravan Club approved workshop facilities, capable of carrying out major repairs. Recovery service available. Calor gas stockists. CORGI registered. **M**

Yorkshire (West)

D.D. CARAVAN SERVICES
Low Mills Lane,
Ravensthorpe Industrial Estate,
Dewsbury WF13 3LX
Tel: 01924 497869

All caravan repairs carried out. **M**

ELECTRO PLATING

Humberside (North)

ALLIANCE ELECTRO PLATING
Valletta Street,
Hedon Road,
Hull HU9 5NP
Tel: 01482 781783

Electro-plating, polishing and powder coating carried out. **M**

FLOORING

DALTONS CARPETS LTD
4 Middle Street,
Hastings TN34 1NA
Tel/Fax: 01424 438395

A family run business established in Hastings. 15 years experience. A good selection of carpets and vinyls at affordable prices. From cords to top Axminsters.

MUSICAL INSTRUMENTS

London

FREDERICK PHELPS (VIOLINS) LTD
67 Fortess Road, NW5 1AD
Tel/Fax: 0171 482 0316

Specialists in fine quality violin family instruments and their bows. We buy, sell, restore and value antique instruments, and also sell ones made by contemporary craftsmen. Full range of accessories stocked. Workshop on the premises. **M**

SUPPLIERS

ARCHITECTURAL IRONMONGERY

Sussex (East & West)

DOCKERILLS (BRIGHTON) LTD

We are a family run business, established for over 85 years, and specialise in architectural ironmongery, brassware, lock-smithing and timber merchandise. Our team of fully qualified tradesmen can tackle almost any job, from fitting locks to making virtually anything from wood. Telephone for more information.

3A, B, C Church Street
Brighton BN1 1UV
Tel: 01273 607434/Fax: 01273 679771
&
9 Church Road, Burgess Hill
Tel: 01444 235994/Fax: 01444 257054

M

West Midlands

DOORFIT PRODUCTS LTD
Icknield House, Heaton Street,
Birmingham B18 5BA
Tel: 0121 554 9291 (24 lines)

Ironmongery of every kind. Cabinet, brass foundry door fittings, sliding tracks. Can carry out exact reproduction replicas of old brass and bronze fittings. M

ARCHITECTURAL SALVAGE

Cambridgeshire

SOLOPARK LTD
The Old Railway Station, Station Road,
Nr Pampisford CB2 4HB
Tel: 01223 834663/Fax: 01223 834780

Suppliers of recycled building materials including

bricks, roofing tiles and slates, joinery and steel. Deliveries arranged. Prices on request.

SOLOPARK LTD
The Old Railway Station,
Station Road, Nr Pampisford CB2 4HB
Tel: 01223 834663/Fax: 01223 834780

BRICKS – All types available – Soft Reds, Handmades, Tudors, Stocks, etc.
ROOFING TILES & SLATES
TIMBERS – STEELS, all sizes and types.
DOORS – Internal and external, hardwood and softwood, stripped or painted. Staircases, window frames, panelling, mouldings etc. Oak and hardwood rafters, studs and beams. Fireplaces, chimney pots, York stone pavings, floor pamments and many other architectural items, etc. Please telephone for brochure.

Specialist suppliers of
RECYCLED BUILDING MATERIALS

CHIMNEYS

Wales - Glamorgan South

MARFLEX CHIMNEY SYSTEMS
Unit 40, Llandow Industrial Estate,
Cowbridge CF7 7PB
Tel: 01446 775551/Fax: 01446 772468

Manufacturers and distributors of refractory concrete chimney systems for building new or renovating old chimneys or dwellings. Liner sizes from 150mm diam. to 760mm square are available. Range includes Multiflex multifuel flexible stainless steel flue linings up to 350mm diam. Free technical service includes chimney sizing, design and material scheduling.

FIREPLACES

Norfolk

NORWICH FIREPLACE CENTRE
Woodside Road, Thorpe,
Norwich NG7 9HA
Tel: 01603 36944
Fax: 01603 700447

Three showrooms with approximately 50 fireplaces on show and nine working living flame gas fires. Also a wide selection of marble and tile hearths, wood mantles, frets, grates and brassware. **M**

FURNISHING TRIMMINGS

London

WENDY A. CUSHING
116 Middleton Road, Dalston E8 4LP
Tel: 0171 249 9709
Fax: 0171 241 3441
Showroom:
M7, Chelsea Garden Market,
Chelsea Harbour, London SW10 0XE
Tel: 0171 351 5796

Specialist trimmings, manufacturers and designers. Restoration and reproduction of tassels, ropes, cords, braids and fringes for curtains, textiles and furniture. Period reproduction of specified designs undertaken. All items are hand woven or handspun by experienced weavers and tassel makers using traditional techniques and equipment.

HEATING & PLUMBING

Surrey

R.W.L. SUPPLIES
93 Burlington Road,
New Malden KT3 4LR
Tel: 0181 942 7677
Fax: 0181 336 2688

Heating, plumbing, bathroom and kitchen supplies.

M

MARQUETRY

Essex

M. L. KEYS (Stephen Keys)
Unit 1,
Hockley Foundry Industrial Estate,
Spa Road, Hockley SS5 4AR
Tel: 01702 200047
Fax: 01268 743473

A small family business manufacturing and retailing an extensive range of exotic wood border inlays, marquetry floral designs and oysters for antique restoration and craft work. A catalogue and price list are available on request.

PAINTS

Essex

LEONARD BROOKS LTD
(Andrew Turner)
Paint Works, Oak Road,
Harold Wood,
Romford RM3 0PL
Tel: 01708 342560
Fax: 01708 377536

Suppliers of all RAL and British Standard bespoke aerosols. At all times 32,000 colours carried in stock. Available in any gloss level. Corporate colours are our speciality. Orders from one to infinity. Free colour matching service available. **M**

PAINT BRUSHES

West Midlands

BEE GEE BRUSHES
Saxon Park Industrial Estate,
Hanbury Road, Stoke Prior,
Bromsgrove B60 4AD
Tel: 01527 837001

Established in 1981, this family-owned business manufactures paint brushes, specialising in all aspects of the paint brush industry, incorporating professional range to the DIY enthusiast. The brushes are handmade to a high specification. Special orders are a feature. **M**

TILES
Sussex (West)

KEYMER HANDMADE CLAY TILES

Tiles manufactured under a Quality Assurance Scheme approved by the British Standard Institute. Clay tiles and fittings are available in a wide choice of colours and an extensive range of ornamental tiles are available in standard shapes including bullnose, club, point, diamond and fishtail. Full range of roof fittings available, i.e. gables, eaves, hips, valleys, ridges and angles.

**Nye Road
Burgess Hill RH15 0LZ
Tel: 01444 232931
Fax: 01444 871852**

WOODFILLERS
Hertfordshire

CLAM-BRUMMER LTD
London Road, Spellbrook,
Nr Bishops Stortford CM23 4BA
Tel: 0171 476 3171/Fax: 0171 474 0098

Brummer woodfillers and grain fillers are manufactured in 13 standard wood colours and are available in two grades; one for interior use and one for exterior use. These products are available on a national scale through builders merchants and hardware distributors, and are widely used by many companies and craftsmen.

COURSES
CERAMICS
Hampshire

MARY ROSE WRANGHAM
25 St Martin's House, Clarence Parade,
Southsea, Portsmouth PO5 2EZ
Tel: 01705 829863

Ceramic restoration courses for one or two students. Suitable for professionals or hobby. Studio hours 10 a.m. - 4 p.m. daily. Also first edition publications. Distance learning in the art of ceramic repair and restoration. Multi-media package – October 1995. Training videos: 1 Beginners; II Advanced.

FURNITURE
Tyne & Wear

THE NORTHERN TRAINING
TRUST LIMITED
7 Tilley Road, Crowther,
Washington NE38 0AE
Tel: 0191 4179696/Fax: 0191 4150955

Charity organisation training pupils in the manufacture of furniture, joinery, construction and other trades.

FURNITURE RESTORATION
Scotland - East Lothian

MYRESIDE INTERNATIONAL SCHOOL OF ANTIQUE FURNITURE RESTORATION
(Principal: Anselm Fraser)
Myreside Grange, Gifford,
East Lothian EH41 4JA
Tel: 01620 810680/Fax: 01620 826285

The Myreside School is an excellent educational establishment for British and foreign students. The career course lasts for a year during which students are taught every aspect of furniture restoration including history and recognition. Excellent facilities and the quality of teaching staff make Myreside internationally recognised. Short specific courses are available.

HELPFUL ORGANISATIONS

A list of organisations able to assist nationally with particular problems – there are many local organisations, guilds and associations which will be very willing to help you.

AKZO NOBEL DECORATIVE COATING
PO Box 37, Hollins Rd, Darwen, Lancashire BB3 0BG
Tel: (01254) 704951

Contact: Trade Marketing Department
Will answer painting queries. Runs a colour scheme service.

ANCIENT MONUMENT SOCIETY
St Ann's Vestry Hall, 2 Church Entry, London EC4V 5HB
Tel: (0171) 236 3934

Contact: Mathew Saunders (Secretary), Tess Powell (Assistant Secretary)
Advises owners of historic or listed houses on restoration, legislation and related subjects. Arranges visits and lectures in Great Britain, and annual study tours to other countries for members. Members receive one volume of transactions each year, plus three newsletters. In partnership with the Friends of Friendless Churches.

ANYTHING LEFT HANDED
57 Brewer St, London W1R 3FB
Tel: (0171) 437 3910

Supplies articles and tools of every description, and much more, for the left-handed person. Send three second class stamps for catalogue.

THE ARCHITECTURAL HERITAGE FUND
27 John Adam St., London WC2N 6HX
Tel: (0171) 925 0199   Fax: (0171) 930 0295

A registered charity, the Fund makes low-interest loans to help other charities preserve and rehabilitate historic buildings threatened by dereliction or destruction.

ARCHITECTURAL SALVAGE
Hutton & Rostron, Netley House, Gomshall, Surrey GU5 9QA
Tel: (014) 83 203221

The architectural salvage index is a register of all types of re-usable building materials and architectural features available throughout the UK. It operates as an agency to put those in need of secondhand materials and items of architectural value directly in contact with those who wish to dispose of them.

THE ASSOCIATION OF BRITISH PICTURE RESTORERS
Station Ave, Kew, Surrey TW9 3QA
Tel/Fax: (0181) 948 5644

Contact: Jan Robinson (Secretary)
Will put you in touch with a nearby restorer. Specialists in particular types of painting.

ASSOCIATION OF INDEPENDENT MUSEUMS (AIM)
Verdants Works, West Hendersons Wynd, Dundee DD2 5BT
Tel: (01382) 225282

Contact: The Secretary
AIM was established to represent the interests of independent museums, to encourage the improvement of their standards through the organisation of seminars, the publication of a bi-monthly bulletin, the publication of guidelines on such matters as charitable status, and the establishment of a new museum. It is AIM's policy to encourage independent museums to adopt charitable trust status to ensure the long-term security of their collections. There are three categories of membership: independent museums or galleries open to the public, controlled by, or registered as, charitable trusts; other independent museums or galleries open to the public; any other bodies, persons, or unincorporated associations who support the aims of the Association.

ASSOCIATION OF MASTER UPHOLSTERERS
Francis Vaughan House, 102 Commercial St, Newport, Gwent NP9 1LU
Tel: (01633) 215454

Contact: Michael Spencer
Investigates complaints on any work undertaken by a member.

THE BASKETMAKER'S ASSOCIATION
Bierton House, 30 Dean Way, Chalfont St Giles, Buckinghamshire HP8 4JL
Tel: (01494) 872296

Contact: Joy Viall (President)
Will put you in touch with members who re-cane, including double caning, blind caning, willow work, baskets, bergere armchairs and side-cars of vintage motorcycles. Rush seating and other rush work. Also members who re-wicker the handles of teapots and jugs. All types of basket-making designed by members. Also supplies lecturers, demonstrators and teachers for all types of basketry and other crafts.

BRITISH ADHESIVES AND SEALANTS ASSOCIATION (BASA)
33 Fellowes Way, Stevenage, Hertfordshire SG2 8BW
Tel: (01438) 358514

Contact: David Williams (Secretary)
Will provide a list of members. Booklet on the safe handling of adhesives in industry is available from members.

BRITISH ANTIQUE DEALERS ASSOCIATION LTD
20 Rutland Gate, London SW9 1BD
Tel: (0171) 589 4128

BRITISH CERAMIC TILE COUNCIL
Federation House, Station Rd, Stoke-On-Trent,
Staffordshire ST4 2RT
Tel: (01782) 747147

Advice on ranges and installation of ceramic wall and floor tiles made by members. For complex enquiries, write to the Council.

BRITISH DECORATORS' ASSOCIATION
32 Coton Rd, Nuneaton, Warwickshire CV11 5TW
Tel: (01203) 353 776

Contact: S. M. Broughton *(Chief Executive)*
A list of firms bound by a code of practice.

BRITISH HOROLOGICAL INSTITUTE
Upton Hall, Upton, Newark, Nottinghamshire NG23 5TE
Tel: (01636) 813795/6

Contact: Helen Bartlett *(Secretary)*

Official testing. Horological educational courses, seminars, etc. Will put you in touch with specialist members. Official journal, *Horological Journal,* published monthly.

BRITISH SOCIETY OF MASTER GLASS-PAINTERS
25 Balmoral Rd, Hitchin, Hertfordshire SG5 1XG
Tel: (01462) 420756

Contact: Sarah Brown *(Secretary)*

Lists of artists and craftsmen in stained glass; advice; booklist; list of courses in stained glass. All members receive the Society's journal once a year, and the magazine twice a year.

THE BRITISH WATCH & CLOCK MAKERS' GUILD
West Wick, Marsh Rd, Burnham-on-Crouch, Essex CM0 8NE
Tel: (01621) 783104

Contact: D. W. Reynolds *(Secretary)*

Members engaged in the manufacture or repair of watches and clocks.

BRITISH WOOD PRESERVING AND DAMP PROOFING ASSOCIATION
Building 6, The Office Village, 4 Romford Rd, Stratford,
London E15 4EA
Tel: (0181) 529 2588   Fax: (0180) 519 3444

Contact: Dr C. R. Coggins

The Association offers a free and impartial advisory service on all aspects of wood preservation, including the remedial and curative treatment of timber *in situ*. Free literature, and lists of specialist companies are available on request.

BRITISH WOODWORKING FEDERATION (BWF)
Broadway House, Tothill St, London SW1H 9NQ
Tel: (0171) 222 1511   Fax: (0171) 222 1577
Contact: D. A. Morgan *(Director)* Michael Lee *(Secretary)*

BWF is a trade association representing the British manufacturers of woodwork for use in building. It provides lists of manufacturers of architectural and general joinery, doors, windows, kitchen furniture, timber frame buildings, laminated structure and timber engineering. Publishes literature for the building professions and for the general public.

BUILDERS MERCHANT'S FEDERATION
15 Soho Sq, London W1V 6HL
Tel: (0171) 439 1753   Fax: (0171) 734 2766

Has 2,300 members nationwide, who provide a helpful, reliable and readily available source of materials. Regional lists available upon application.

THE BUILDING CENTRE
26 Store St, London WC1E 7BT
Tel: (0171) 439 1753

Information on the most suitable materials and fittings for redecoration or re-building schemes.

THE BUILDING CONSERVATION TRUST
– see UPKEEP

THE BUILDING INFORMATION CENTRE
Stoke-On-Trent College, Stoke Rd, Shelton,
Stoke-On-Trent, Staffordshire ST4 2DG
Tel: (01782) 208208   Fax: (01782) 203554

Information relating to the building trade, British Standards and codes of practice.

BUILDING RESEARCH ESTABLISHMENT
Garston, Watford, Hertfordshire WD2 7JR
Tel: (01923) 894040

Intermediate research and development on a wide range of construction technology. Advisory service. Sells publications.

CATHEDRALS FABRIC COMMISSION FOR ENGLAND
Fielden House, Little College St, London SW1P 3SH
Tel: (0171) 222 3793
Contact: Dr Richard Gem

Advises Deans/Provosts and Chapters of cathedrals (chiefly in England, but also in Wales and Scotland) on all matters to do with the care and conservation of their cathedral churches and closely related structures, and their historic furnishings and fittings. Advises on the suitability and appointment of architects, designers, archeologists, art historians, and other specialists. Maintains (with the Council for the Care of Churches) an index of artists and craftsmen.

CHARTERED SOCIETY OF DESIGNERS
29 Bedford Sq, London WC1B 3EG
Tel: (0171) 631 1510
Contact: John Berridge (Publicity Officer)

CHIMNEY ADVISORY SERVICE
c/o CICO Ltd, Westleton, Saxmundham, Suffolk IP17 3BS
Tel: (01728) 648 608
Provides advice on the correction of chimney problems, and the building of new chimneys.

CIVIC TRUST
17 Carlton House Terrace, London SW1Y 5AW
(Associate trusts in Glasgow, Cardiff, Manchester and Newcastle-upon-Tyne)
Tel: (0171) 930 0914

Contact: The Director

Works to protect and improve the environment. Produces a bi-monthly journal, Heritage Outlook, and other publications.

COLLEGE OF MASONS
42 Magdalen Rd, Wandsworth, London SW18 3NP
Tel: (0181) 874 8363

Contact: The Secretary

Members include masons for marble, stone, granite, slate and knap flint.

CONSERVATION BUREAU, SCOTTISH DEVELOPMENT AGENCY
– see LOTHIAN AND EDINBURGH ENTERPRISES LTD

CONSUMERS' ASSOCIATION
2 Marylebone Rd, London NW1 4DF
Tel: (0171) 486 5544
Variety of helpful publications on many aspects of repair, etc., available direct. Send for full details.

COPPER DEVELOPMENT ASSOCIATION
Orchard House, Mutton Lane, Potters Bar,
Hertfordshire EN6 3AP
Tel: (01707) 650711

Contact: Information Department

Information and advice on copper and copper alloys.

COUNCIL FOR THE CARE OF CHURCHES
Fielden House, Little College St, London SW1P 3SH
Tel: (0171) 222 3793

Contact: Conservation Officer

Information and advice on the conservation of churches and their furnishings; allocation of grant aid for the conservation of furnishings and works of art in churches.

CRAFTS COUNCIL
44A Pentonville Rd, London NW 9BY
Tel: (0171) 278 7700

The Crafts Council administers an annual government grant for the support of crafts in England and Wales, and the promotions of the work of artists/craftspeople. Facilities include a gallery at Waterloo Place with a changing programme of exhibitions, an information centre, slide library and bookstall. The Council provides grants, loans and bursaries, publishes the bi-monthly magazine Crafts, and a range of other books, postcards and slide packs. There is an education section which works at school and college levels, and the Council also manages the Craft Council shop at the Victoria and Albert Museum. Funding is given to the Welsh Arts Council, regional arts associations and Contemporary Applied Arts, a membership organisation for craftspeople which holds exhibitions and sells work through its gallery in Covent Garden, London. Scotland receives a separate government grant.

CRAFTSMEN POTTERS' ASSOCIATION OF GREAT BRITAIN
7 Marshall St, London W1V 1LP
Tel: (0171) 437 7605

Provides a list of members, and a list of courses available. A retail outlet and exhibition centre for members' work.

DRAUGHT PROOFING ADVISORY ASSOCIATION LTD
PO Box 12, Haslemere, Surrey GU27 3AH
Tel: (01428) 654011

Contact: Gillian A. Allder

Write for list of members and informative literature.

DRY STONE WALLING ASSOCIATION
YFC Centre, National Agricultural Centre,
Stoneleigh Park, Warwickshire CV8 2LG
Tel: (0121) 378 0493

Contact: Mrs J. Simkins (Secretary)

Register of recommended craftsmen. Quarterly newsletter to members. Guide to publications on walling. General advisory service. Memberships available: professional, open, junior and corporate. Skills certificate also available.

ELECTRICAL CONTRACTORS' ASSOCIATION
ESCA House, 34 Palace Court, London W2 4JG
Tel: (0171) 229 1266

Contact: John Clarke

All members' work is guaranteed.

EMBROIDERERS' GUILD
Apartment 41, Hampton Court Palace, East Molesey, Surrey KT8 9AU
Tel: (0181) 943 1229

Does not undertake restoration, but is an educational charity, founded in 1906 to promote the craft of embroidery to the highest possible standards. This it does through workshops and lectures, seminars, conferences and exhibitions, and through the activities of over 140 affiliated branches, and its quarterly magazine, *The World of Embroidery*. Collection of historic and modern embroidery and lace. Open to the public from time to time.

ENGLISH HERITAGE
Fortress House, 23 Savile Row, London W1X 2AB
Tel: (0171)973 3000

Advises the Secretary of State for the Environment on the making of grants to outstanding individual buildings, churches in use, buildings in conservation areas, and town schemes.

EXTERNAL WALL INSULATION ASSOCIATION
PO Box 12, Haslemere, Surrey GU27 3AH
Tel: (01428) 654011

Contact: Gillian A. Allder

Write for list of members and informative literature.

FEDERATION OF MASTER BUILDERS
Gordon Fisher House, 14–15 Great James St, London WC1N 5DP
Tel: (0171) 242 7583

Trade association for over 21,500 builders nationwide, mostly medium-sized, in all aspects of building work. Will recommend local members. Warranty scheme.

FELLOWSHIP OF MAKERS AND RESEARCHERS OF HISTORICAL INSTRUMENTS (FOMRHI)
171 Iffley Rd, Oxford, Oxfordshire OX4 1EL
E Mail: J Montagu VAX.OX.AC.UK

Contact: Jeremy Montagu (*Honorary Secretary*)

FoMRHI was founded in 1975 as an organisation of people concerned with historical musical instruments. Its aim is to promote authenticity in the preservation of original instruments, in making reproductions of such instruments, and in the use of both. Membership is open to anyone interested in any of these aspects. All members receive *FoMRHI Quarterly*, which includes a bulletin of practical and research information, requests for information, notes and queries, news and views, and a number of communications. These are of widely varying length, and range from the speculative to the thoroughly researched, and from the practical to the theoretical and the philosophical.

GLASS & GLAZING FEDERATION
44–48 Borough High St, London SE1 1XB
Tel: (0171) 403 7177

Provides one central source of advice to architects, builders and householders on all matters relating to the use of glass and glazing methods.

GUILD OF ARCHITECTURAL IRONMONGERS
8 Stepney Green, London E1 3JU
Tel: (0171) 790 3431   Fax: (0180) 790 8517

List of members (companies who are qualified architectural ironmongers having a member of their staff who has passed the Guild's examinations). *Architectural Ironmongers Journal*, quarterly. Code of practice.

THE GUILD OF MASTER CRAFTSMEN
Castle Place, 166 High Street, Lewes, East Sussex BN7 1XU
Tel: (01273) 478449   Fax: (01273) 478606

Contact: The Information Officer

The membership of the Guild of Master Craftsmen covers a variety of skills and trades including construction, repair and restoration, traditional crafts, professional and consultancy services, mechanical skills and engineering, and a growing service and retail membership. Its aims and objectives are to promote high standards of skill and quality of service in all members' activities, and to provide those members with marketing opportunities and business benefits. Its sister company, Guild of Master Craftsman Publications, is a well–recognised publisher of woodworking and craft books, magazines and videos. For details of members in your area, or information on applying for membership, contact the Information Officer.

GUILD OF TAXIDERMISTS
Taxidermy Section, Museums and Art Galleries, Kelvingrove, Glasgow G3 8AG
Tel: (0141) 221 9600

Contact: Duncan Ferguson (*Secretary*)

Gives advice and will put you in touch with taxidermist members in particular areas.

HAMILTON BILLIARDS AND GAMES COMPANY
Park Lane, Knebworth, Hertfordshire SG3 6PG
Tel: (01438) 811995

Specialists in period billiard tables. Makers of traditional indoor and outdoor games – chess, table tennis, croquet etc.

HAMPSHIRE BUILDINGS PRESERVATION TRUST LTD
The Castle, Winchester, Hampshire SO23 8UE
Tel: (01962) 841841, ext. 6719

Contact: Deane Clark (*Head of Historic Buildings Bureau*)

Concerned with the conservation of local buildings, runs practical courses on historic building conservation, offers help and advice.

HEATING AND VENTILATING CONTRACTORS' ASSOCIATION
ESCA House, 34 Palace Court, Bayswater, London W2 4JG
Tel: (0171) 229 2488

Write or phone for a local member for domestic central heating installations, repairs and maintenance. Write for a list of members involved in industrial and commercial heating, air conditioning, refrigeration, fire protection and related work, including duct work.

HISTORIC HOUSES ASSOCIATION
2 Chester St, London SW1X 7BB
Tel: *(0171) 259 5688*

Contact: Terence Empson *(Director General)*

An association of owners and guardians of historic houses, parks, gardens and places of interest (and their associated contents) of Great Britain: formed to promote and safeguard their legitimate interests so far as they are consistent with the interests of the nation.

INFIL LTD
Infil House, Hadnall, Shrewsbury, Shropshire SY4 4AG
Tel: *(01939) 21 0320*

Infil is a chemical compound (not foam) sprayed to the underside of unfelted tiled or slate roofs, securing the fixings and sealing the entire inside of the roof against the penetration of rain, snow and cold winds. Cuts re-roofing costs drastically, and is undetectable from the outside.

THE KITCHEN SPECIALISTS' ASSOCIATION
PO Box 311, Worcester WR1 1DN
Tel: *(01905) 726066*

Addresses of local members available. Shops specialise in kitchen design, supply and installation.

THE LANDSCAPE INSTITUTE
6–7 Bernard Mews, London SW11 1QU
Tel: *(0171) 738 9166*

The professional institute for landscape architects, landscape managers, and landscape scientists. Publishes a journal, *Landscape Design*, 10 times a year.

THE LIGHTING ASSOCIATION LTD
Stafford Park 7, Telford, Shropshire TS3 3BQ
Tel: *(01952) 290905   Fax: (01952) 290906*

Contact: The Director

Represents the manufacturing end of the UK's lighting industry. A full technical advisory service is provided, including an opportunity to partake in the Lighting Association Code of Practice. The Association organises trade exhibitions and provides the opportunity to advertise at special member rates in the exhibition catalogue, which has a circulation of over 6,000, to companies directly associated with the lighting industry. An annual buyers' guide is produced in collaboration with *Lighting Equipment News*, listing all members, addresses and basic product details. The guide is distributed to all retailers, architects and contractors and is available on request. A keen interest is taken in the career development of young designers. Sponsors and organises an annual competition in colleges of design throughout the UK. *Lighting Magazine* is published every two months and circulated within the lighting industry and associated trades.

LONDON AND PROVINCIAL ANTIQUE DEALERS' ASSOCIATION (LAPADA)
535 Kings Rd, Chelsea, London SW10 0SZ
Tel: *(0171) 823 3511*

Details of restorer members may be obtained from the Secretary.

LOTHIAN AND EDINBURGH ENTERPRISES LTD
Apex House, 99 Haymarket Tce, Edinburgh EH12 5HD
Tel: *(0131) 313 4000*

Helps all those concerned with the conservation of historic buildings and objects. Offers advice on conservation skills, sources of materials and technical and historical information.

MASTER LOCKSMITHS' ASSOCIATION
Units 4 and 5, The Business Park, Woodford Halse, Daventry, Northamptonshire NN11 3PZ
Tel: *(01327) 262255   Fax: (01327) 262539*

Contact: Roman Russocki

Will recommend local members: 1,500 members nationwide. Publishes *Keyways* bi-monthly for members.

MEN OF THE STONES
25 Cromarty Rd, Stamford, Lincolnshire PE9 2TQ
Tel: *(01780) 53527*

Contact: Mrs MacKenzie-Ross *(Secretary)*

Will put you in touch with appropriate masons, architects and quarries. Gives advice on conservation of ancient stonework.

MONUMENTAL BRASS SOCIETY
c/o Society of Antiquaries, Burlington House, Piccadilly, London W1V 0HS

Contact: W. Mendelsson *(Honorary Secretary)*

The object of the society is to study, care for and repair monumental brasses. Able to direct the repair of brasses. There is a bulletin three times a year, plus various other publications. Contact the Honorary Secretary for details.

MUSEUMS AND GALLERIES COMMISSION
Conservation Unit, 16 Queen Anne's Gate, London SW1H 9AA
Tel: *(0171) 233 4200   Fax: (0171) 233 3686*

Set up in April 1987 to foster conservation generally and to ensure that the needs and the views of private conservators, who represent a large proportion of conservation expertise in the country, receive proper attention. The Unit has established a UK register of conservators and restorers. General conservation information service.

NATIONAL ASSOCIATION OF FARRIERS, BLACKSMITHS & AGRICULTURAL ENGINEERS
Avenue R, 7th St, NAC Stoneleigh, Warwickshire CV8 2LG
Tel: (01203) 696595   Fax: (01203) 696708
Restoration of wrought iron work on buildings. Bi-monthly *Forge* magazine. Trade association membership available.

NATIONAL ASSOCIATION OF LOFT INSULATION CONTRACTORS
PO Box 12, Haslemere, Surrey GU27 3AH
Tel: (01428) 654011
Contact: Gillian A. Allder
Write for list of members and informative literature.

NATIONAL ASSOCIATION OF MEMORIAL MASONS
Crown Buildings, High St, Aylesbury,
Buckinghamshire HP20 1SL
Tel: (01296) 434750
Contact: Theresa Quinn *(National Executive Officer)*
The Association represents stone masons who specialise in memorial work. It represents both wholesale and retail sides of the trade, and publishes a quarterly journal, for members only. Through its external committee, the Association advises churches and local authorities on the provision of memorials in churchyards and cemeteries, and on the design of cemeteries. The Association holds an annual conference, including a trade exhibition and a craft competition. The Association is the managing agent for a youth course in memorial masonry.

NATIONAL BED FEDERATION LTD (NBF)
251 Brompton Rd, London SW3 2EZ
Tel: (0171) 589 4888   Fax: (0171) 823 7009
The NBF provides information and advice on beds, varying from product availability and type for trade enquiries, to general consumer advice about buying beds. Leaflets and fact sheets available on request (send a 36p stamped addressed envelope).

NATIONAL CARPET CLEANERS' ASSOCIATION
126 New Walk, De Montfort St, Leicester LE1 7JA
Tel: (0116) 255 4352
Contact: Pam King *(General Secretary)*
Authority on all aspects of carpet and upholstery maintenance.

NATIONAL CAVITY INSULATION
PO Box 12, Haslemere, Surrey GU27 3AH
Tel: (01428) 654011
Contact: Gillian A. Allder
Write for list of members, details of loan scheme, and informative literature.

THE NATIONAL FEDERATION OF ROOFING CONTRACTORS
24 Weymouth St, London W1N 4LX
Tel: (0171) 436 0387
Contact: A. E. S. Cowan OBE *(Chief Executive)*
Will send list of local members who carry out repairs or renew complete roof. Send stamped, addressed envelope.

THE NATIONAL FEDERATION OF TERRAZZO, MARBLE AND MOSAIC SPECIALISTS
PO Box 50, Banstead, Surrey SM7 2RD
Tel: (01737) 360673
Recommends and undertakes repair work. Carries out expert investigation into complaints in respect of terrazzo, marble and mosaic work for a fee.

NATIONAL FIREPLACE ASSOCIATION
8th Floor, Bridge House, Smallbrook, Queensway, Birmingham B5 4JP
Tel: (0121) 643 3377   Fax: (0121) 643 5064
Contact: David Brotherton *(Director)*

NATIONAL ASSOCIATION OF MASTER THATCHERS
73 Hughenden Ave, Downley, High Wycombe, Buckinghamshire HP13 5SL
Tel: (01494) 443198   Fax: (01494) 445597
Contact: Christopher White
Can supply names and addresses of members in particular areas. Advice to architects, builders and house owners on all types of thatching, roof construction and insurance etc.

PEWTER SOCIETY
Hunters Lodge, Paddock Cl, St Mary's Platt, Sevenoaks, Kent TN15 8NN
Tel: (01732) 883314
Contact: Dr J. Richardson *(Secretary)*
Advice on restoration and conservation of old pewter.

ROYAL INSTITUTE OF BRITISH ARCHITECTS
66 Portland Pl, London W1N 4AD
Tel: (0171) 222 7000
Contact: Information Centre
Will give names of chartered surveyors to undertake surveys and supervise rehabilitation and repair work. Will give the names of local members able to carry out surveys on any property. Various information leaflets available.

ROYAL SCHOOL OF NEEDLEWORK
Apartment 12A, Hampton Court Palace, Surrey KT8 9AU
Tel: (0181) 943 1432

Undertakes conservation, restoration and repair of tapestries, tapestry seat coverings, regimental colours, embroidery, lace and other textiles. Classes in all aspects of embroidery. Call by appointment only. Small shop open to the public 9am to 5pm, Monday to Friday.

RURAL DEVELOPMENT COMMISSION
141 Castle St, Salisbury, Wiltshire SP1 3TP
Tel: (01722) 336255

Thirty-two businesses service offices in England. Training courses geared specifically to the needs of the small rural business. Also technical and business advice for small rural firms available. Various publications. Write for details.

SOCIETY OF FINE ART AUCTIONEERS
7 Blenheim St, New Bond St, London W1Y 0AS
Tel: (0171) 629 2933

Contact: Miss M. Swain *(Secretary)*, (0476) 590176

The Society is a professional body representing fine art auctioneers throughout the country. A free booklet is available, giving names and addresses of members, and details about the Society.

THE SOCIETY FOR THE PROTECTION OF ANCIENT BUILDINGS
37 Spital Sq, London E1 6DY
Tel: (0171) 377 1644

Contact: Philip Venning *(Secretary)*

The Society publishes technical pamphlets, offers technical advice on the repair of old buildings through the Technical Panel, and runs nine-month scholarships as part of training for architects, surveyors, engineers and builders. Names of architects, builders and suppliers are available on request. Provides specialist information on wind and watermills through the Wind and Watermill Section. Runs two six-day courses per year, in April and October. Provides tours, lectures and technical visits. Quarterly newsletter and housing list for members. William Morris Fellowship for building craftsmen. Weekend repair course in February.

THE STONE FEDERATION
18 Mansfield St, London W1M 9FG
Tel: (0171) 580 5404   Fax: (0171) 636 5984

Contact: Miss J. E. Buxey

Trade association representing companies engaged in all aspects of the natural stone industry, including quarries, suppliers, fixers, stonemasons and stone cleaning contractors. Write for a list of members.

THE TEXTILE CONSERVATION CENTRE
Apartment 22, Hampton Court Palace, East Molesey,
Surrey KT8 9AU
Tel: (0181) 977 4943

Experts in conservation of large woven tapestries, lace, ceremonial pieces, flags, colours, upholstery and costumes etc. Advisory service available. Training in textile conservation. Write for information.

TEXTILE SERVICES ASSOCIATION LTD
(Dry-cleaning Information Bureau)
7 Churchill Crt, 58 Station Rd, North Harrow, Middlesex HA2 7SA
Tel: (0181) 863 7755

Can provide details of cleaners offering specialist services.

THATCHING ADVISORY SERVICE LTD
Faircross Offices, Stratfield Way, Reading, Berkshire RG7 2BT
Tel: (01256) 880828

Specialists in thatched property insurance. Offering total service to owners of thatched property including surveys, free quotes, re-thatching etc.

TIMBER RESEARCH & DEVELOPMENT ASSOCIATION (TRADA)
Stocking Lane, Hughenden Valley, High Wycombe,
Buckinghamshire HP14 4ND
Tel: (01494) 563091

UPKEEP
The Trust for Training and Education in Building Maintenance
Apartment 39, Hampton Court Palace, East Molesey,
Surrey KT8 9BS
Tel: (0181) 943 2277   Fax: (0181) 943 9552

Contact: John Metcalf *(Director)*

The Trust organises *Care of Buildings*, a permanent exhibition of techniques and materials. Open to the public. Telephone for times, charges and party bookings. Training courses for staff of local authorities and housing associations.

VEHICLE BUILDERS AND REPAIRERS' ASSOCIATION
Belmont House, Finkle Lane, Gildersome, Leeds LS27 7TW
Tel: (01532) 538333

Free advice on where to get repairs and restoration work on cars and commercial vehicles.

THE WORSHIPFUL COMPANY OF COACHMAKERS AND COACH HARNESS MAKERS
149 Banstead Rd, Ewell, Epsom, Surrey KT17 3HL
Tel: (0181) 393 5394

Contact: Major W. H. Wharfe

General information on the repair, restoration and conservation of horse-drawn carriages. Information on craftsmen who repair and manufacture carriage harnesses. Information on organisations who manufacture new, modern horse-drawn carriages.

PUBLICATIONS INDEX

ANTIQUE COLLECTING
The Antique Collectors' Club Ltd
5 Church St, Woodbridge
Suffolk IP12 1DS
Tel: (01394) 385501

Published: 10 issues per year

Price: single copy £2.50: per year £19.50

Articles giving expert advice and practical information to collectors and anyone with an interest in antiques. There is an annual investment issue, and listings of auctions, fairs, saleroom prices, and collectors' clubs.

BUILD IT
Build It Publications Ltd
37 High St, Kingston KT1 1LQ
Tel: (0181) 549 2166

Published: monthly

Price: single copy £1.95

Provides guidance for all aspects of successful self-built projects. Covers readers' homes, finance, design, interiors, land, plans and costings, and new products.

CHURCH BUILDING
Gabriel Communications Ltd
1st Floor St James's Buildings, Oxford St
Manchester M1 6FP
Tel: (0161) 236 8856

Published: 6 issues per year

Price: single copy £3.00

Covers all aspects of church design and construction, with technical studies, arts and crafts features, and project reports.

COMPLETE INTERIORS
M & M Creative Services
Hillrising House, 115 Potters Lane,
Send, Nr Woking, Surrey GU23 7AW
Tel: (01483) 750692

Published: quarterly

Price: single copy £1.50: per year £5.00

Covers interior furnishing, design and decoration, with regular features on antiques, gardening and plants, and property.

THE GARDEN
EMAP Apex Publications Ltd
Apex House, Oundle Rd, Peterborough PE2 9NP
Tel: (01733) 898100

Published: monthly

Price: single copy £2.50

This is the journal of the Royal Horticultural Society. Covers all horticultural topics, written by experts. Contains news and listings of horticultural events.

GOOD HOUSEKEEPING
National Magazine Co Ltd
National Magazine House, 72 Broadwick St
London W1V 2BP
Tel: (0171) 439 5000

Published: monthly

Price: single copy £1.80

A complete lifestyle magazine focused on family and home. Covers homes, gardening and other consumer features. The Good Housekeeping Institute answers readers' enquiries on general repairs, stain removal etc, for letters accompanied with a stamped, addressed envelope.

HOUSEBUILDER
Housebuilder Publications Ltd
82 New Cavendish St, London W1M 8AD
Tel: (0171) 580 5588

Published: 10 issues per year

Price: single copy £6.00

Covers political, economic, technical and development issues for both private and social housing. Regular features on conservation, regional and town planning, technical information services, environment and associations.

IDEAL HOME
IPC Magazines
King's Reach Tower, Stamford St, London SE1 9LS
Tel: (0171) 261 5360

Published: monthly

Price: single copy £1.65

Covers all aspects of the home environment, with practical advice, regular buyers guides, and features concerned with making and maintaining a home.

LANDSCAPE DESIGN
Coleman Lyttle and Co Ltd
13a West St, Reigate, Surrey RH2 9BL
Tel: (01737) 225374

Published: 10 issues per year

Price: per year £33

The official *Journal of the Landscape Institute* supplement.

PERIOD HOUSE AND ITS GARDEN
Orpheus Publications
7 St. Johns Rd, Harrow, Middlesex HA1 2EE
Tel: (0181) 863 2020

Published: monthly

Price: single copy £2.20

Provides ideas and guidance for renovating, decorating and furnishing period houses. Each issue includes news, and useful addresses.

PERIOD LIVING AND TRADITIONAL HOMES

EMAP Elan Ltd
Victory House, 14 Leicester Pl, London WC2H 7BP
Tel: (0171) 437 9011

Published: monthly

Price: single copy £2.20

Magazine for people living in older houses (pre 1939). Combines practical information with inspirational photography and ideas. Each issue includes a renovation directory of regional suppliers of period fixtures and fittings.

PRACTICAL GARDENING

EMAP Apex Publications Ltd
Apex House, Oundle Rd, Peterborough PE2 9NP
Tel: (01733) 898100

Price: single copy £2.00: per year £22.80

Provides creative and design-related advice and ideas.

PRACTICAL HOUSEHOLDER

Nexus Media Ltd
Warwick House, Azalea Dr, Swanley, Kent BR8 8HY
Tel: (01322) 660070

Published: monthly

Price: single copy £1.60

Covers all aspects of DIY, both inside and outside. Practical articles on restoring and repairing furniture. Advice on choosing tradesmen, and reviews of tools and equipment.

SPECIALIST BUILDING FINISHES

Herald House Ltd
Herald House, 96 Dominion Rd, Worthing
West Sussex BN14 8JP
Tel: (01903) 821082

Published: 4 issues per year

Price: single copy £4.00

A magazine for specialist contractors and specifiers of building finishes, especially plaster and plasterboard. Areas covered include walls, ceilings, floors and rendering.

THE WORLD OF INTERIORS

The Conde Nast Publications Ltd
Vogue House, Hanover Sq, London WIR 0AD
Tel: (0171) 499 9080

Published: monthly

Price: single copy £2.90: per year £37

Covers all aspects of interior design/decoration for period and modern homes, and public buildings. Carries in-depth articles on furniture, craftsmen, merchandise, fabrics, wall coverings and specialist shops.

PUBLICATIONS AVAILABLE FROM GMC

WOODTURNING

ADVENTURES IN WOODTURNING

David Springett

More projects from wizard woodturner David Springett for you to enjoy. Packed full of surprises and mind-boggling trickery, these 20 projects are sure to inspire. Create a variation of the ship-in-a-bottle trick, a barrel that only opens when you spin it, and an egg only you will know how to balance.

MULTI-CENTRE WOODTURNING

Ray Hopper

Multi and off-centre turning, fascinating developments of the craft of woodturning, are covered in depth in this book. The exciting projects range from the practical to the decorative, and include imaginative fantasies inspired by the wood itself. Photos, plans and line drawings accompany the clear instructions, and safety measures are included in each chapter.

USEFUL WOODTURNING PROJECTS

GMC Publications

The ideal book if you are looking for a varied and stimulating range of inspirational pieces to create on the lathe. The fully-illustrated projects provide you with detailed step-by-step information, and the world's top turners give tips and hints gained from their years of experience.

WOODTURNING: A FOUNDATION COURSE

Keith Rowley

For all woodturners, this book guides you through every aspect of turning, advises you on which tools to buy and which lathe to choose, and concludes with eight carefully designed and well-illustrated projects.

WOODTURNING: A SOURCE BOOK OF SHAPES
John Hunnex

Over 100 superb lathe-turned shapes which serve as an inspiration and a standard for novices and experienced turners alike. The nine categories, from bowls to vases, include a short preface on form and design. Presented in stunning colour, these magnificent pieces are a tribute to the author's background both as a master woodturner and as a lecturer in photography.

WOODTURNING TECHNIQUES
GMC Publications

Over the years, *Woodturning* magazine has featured a wide range of fascinating articles on techniques from woodturners all over the world. This book brings together a collection of over 20 of the best of these articles for you to read and refer to, and is illustrated throughout with line drawings and photographs. Varied and informative, this book is a must for every woodturner's library.

WOODTURNING WIZARDRY
David Springett

Twenty intriguing projects to test your skills. With David's expert guidance, what appears impossible becomes possible, and the secrets of turning cubes in spheres, stars in cubes, and interlocking spheres are revealed. Detailed guidance is given on precision marking, constructing jigs and chucks, and making and adapting tools.

WOODCARVING

DECORATIVE WOODCARVING
Jeremy Williams

The complete companion for the beginner, this step-by-step guide will also be of interest to professionals wishing to extend their skills. The book takes you through a structured series of simple, intermediate, and advanced relief carving projects, to help you gain an in-depth understanding and mastery of techniques.

WOODCARVING TOOLS, MATERIALS AND EQUIPMENT
Chris Pye

How should I hold this? How can I sharpen that? Why does this slip? If you've ever asked yourself these or similar questions, then this is where to look. This extraordinarily detailed reference book has been meticulously researched to help you choose the correct tools, and to use them as effectively and safely as possible.

FURNITURE AND UPHOLSTERY

FURNITURE PROJECTS
Rod Wales

One of Britain's leading designers and craftsmen shares his design processes and presents a range of beautiful and practical furniture to delight both aspiring and experienced craftsmen: complete with detailed text, dimensioned plans and explanatory photographs.

FURNITURE RESTORATION AND REPAIR FOR BEGINNERS
Kevin Jan Bonner

The book to answer your every question on restoring furniture from Chippendale to chipboard; from stripping to staining; from wax finishes to water-based varnishes. Learn how to fix a wobbly chair or a scratched table top, how to identify and repair finishes and veneers, how to stain wood, apply a French polish finish or remove white ring marks.

MAKING FINE FURNITURE
Tom Darby

The 12 new projects in this book, by leading Australian designer/makers, offer a unique insight into the design processes and construction techniques of a dozen talented professionals.

MAKING SHAKER FURNITURE
Barry Jackson

From a master craftsman with an interest in this unique American religious sect come 13 superb projects based on traditional Shaker pieces. Each project is presented in detail, with accompanying drawings and clear photographs.

THE UPHOLSTERER'S POCKET REFERENCE BOOK
David James

All the information an upholsterer needs contained in one handy-sized volume. Facts, figures, formulae, calculations and regulations are at your fingertips to save you time, money and ordering mistakes. Advice is given on workshop layout, equipment and safety, measuring, cutting, estimating, costing and conversions, and guidance given on the selection and use of fabrics, hides, leathers, coverings, trimmings and decorations.

UPHOLSTERY: A COMPLETE GUIDE
David James

A comprehensive book providing you with both the theory and techniques of upholstery, including tools and materials to use, plus techniques for many styles of furniture. Required reading for professionals, students and amateurs, this book gives thorough advice on selecting, specifying and purchasing materials.

UPHOLSTERY TECHNIQUES AND PROJECTS
David James

Thirty detailed projects representing over 400 years of upholstery design make this the essential book on practical upholstery. An indispensable companion for upholsterers of all abilities, this book is in colour throughout, and includes 60 photographs and over 300 line drawings depicting every aspect of the craft in fine detail.

TOOLS AND THE WORKSHOP

ELECTRIC WOODWORK: POWER TOOL WOODWORKING
Jeremy Broun

Ten of todays most popular power tools and their accessories are examined in detail, and their uses and capabilities (conventional and unconventional) explained by an award-winning craftsman. Hundreds of line drawings and photographs complement the 12 specially designed projects, to help you make the most of the tools described.

MAKING AND MODIFYING WOODWORKING TOOLS
Jim Kingshott

Old woodworking tools have a romance, fascination and value all of their own. More than that, a properly functioning hand tool of the classic style can bring you superlative results. Jim Kingshott's book shows you how to make and adapt vices, saw and chisel handles, as well as modify and improve planes, forge screwdrivers, and how to improve and create handles for a wide range of tools.

SHARPENING: THE COMPLETE GUIDE
Jim Kingshott

All woodworkers recognise the joy of using razor-sharp tools, but many struggle to obtain those elusive, perfect edges. Now you can share in the secrets of sharpening techniques with guidance from professional cabinet maker, Jim Kingshott. Extensively illustrated and detailed, this book offers advice gleaned from many years experience.

THE WORKSHOP: DESIGNING BUILDING EQUIPPING
Jim Kingshott

Your comprehensive guide to designing, planning and equipping a workshop whatever the size, so that it is well equipped, space and cost efficient. This well-illustrated handbook covers planning, construction, conversions, regulations and safety, services, storage and care, the bench, tools and machinery, and sharpening equipment.

PRACTICAL CRAFTS

FRAMING AND GILDING
Paul Curson

Techniques and formulae for making and restoring picture frames with tools, described in detail. This book also provides a comprehensive introduction to gilding for any wooden surface, and features over 100 photographs and drawings, with an additional 50 frame designs.

MARQUETRY
David Hume

David Hume gives you step-by-step instructions for sources of wood and cutting the wood into veneers, making a marquetry picture from start to finish, and dealing with geometric patterns (parquetry). He also suggests solutions for some of the faults which can arise. A range of illustrated design ideas is included, featuring birds, landscapes, buildings, boats and abstract pictures.

SEAT WEAVING
Ricky Holdstock

Bringing life to old and well-loved furniture is very rewarding, and re-seating a chair is now brought within your reach with this comprehensive book. All techniques for weaving in rush, cane, seagrass and cord are covered here, including patterns such as the Double Victoria, the Spider's Web and the Rising Sun.

WOODFINISHING HANDBOOK
(published October 1995)
Ian Hosker

This handy pocket book answers all your questions on how to achieve the ultimate finish on your work. Ian Hosker dispels the myth that the art of woodfinishing is difficult to master. The practical advice, quick reference tables, and glossary of terms provide all the knowledge you need to achieve professional results. Covers preparation, staining, bleaching, wax and oil polishing, French polishing, colouring, varnishing and much more.

Classifieds

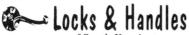

COX'S YARD

ARCHITECTURAL ANTIQUES,
EFFECTS AND RECLAMATION
OAK, ELM AND PITCH PINE
BEAMS AND BOARDS, FIRE
PLACES AND SURROUNDS

"FROM A BEAM TO A BRICK
FROM A FLAG TO A FIRE
FROM A SLATE TO A STATUE
FROM A FLOOR TO A DOOR
AND MUCH, MUCH MORE!"

ALL RECLAIMED BUILDING
MATERIALS BOUGHT AND SOLD

COXS YARD, THE OLD DAIRY,
FOSSE WAY INDUSTRIAL ESTATE
MORETON IN MARSH
GLOS. GL56 9NQ

TEL/FAX: 01608 652505

 OURSES

Restoration Courses

FURNITURE RESTORATION COURSES

3 & 5 days. Also: French Polishing, Veneering,
Marquetry, Upholstery, Can/Rush. Maximum 4 students.
Accommodation list.

Graham Usher, B.A.F.R.A..
Fairhope Fine Furniture Restoration Courses,
5 Rose Terrace, Mitchell, Nr Newquay, Cornwall TR8 5AU
Tel: 01872 510551

Woodland Craft Courses

in West Wales, Oxfordshire, Suffolk, this
Summer. Pole Lathe turning stool/hurdle
making coppice crafts. SAE for details -

Felin Dolfor, Pencader, Dyfed, SA39 9JD.
Tel: 01570 423203

SPINNING & WEAVING SUPPLIES

Weekend courses, wide range of Fibre/Fleece/
Yarns/Equipment/Books/Dyes, E.A.,
mail order and personal callers welcome.

Please send stamp for catalogue.
Open 10am-5pm Tues to Sat
the handweavers studio & gallery ltd
29 Haroldstone Rd, London E17 7AN
Tel: 0181 521 2281

UPHOLSTERY WORKSHOP
Members of the Association of Master Upholsterers
Career change, taking up a hobby?

Learn the professional way, Individual tuition by
master upholsterer. Residential courses in idyllic
surroundings. Rural Wales.

**Details: The Upholstery
Workshop, Teify View,
Llandyfriog, Newcastle
Emlyn, Dyfed SA38 9HB
Tel: 01239 711265**

Courses offered in Soft Furnishings

Curtains, Swags & Tails, Pelmets, Loose-covers,
Headboards, Bedspreads, Lampshades, Blinds,
Upholstery, Caning & Rush courses also available.
To Professional Standard.

Apply: **Natural Resources Workshop,
14 Alton Road, Luton, Beds. LU1 3NS
Tel: 01582 481216**

YORK COLLEGE
of Further and Higher Education

ANTIQUE FURNITURE RESTORATION

The School of Construction have places in Furniture
Restoration and Conservation, offering the choice of both
full time and part time courses for a City and Guilds 564/7 &
555 awards. Also courses available City & Guilds/COTAC
Master Crafts Diploma in Restoration and Conservation.
For further details contact: Mr R Silk, York College of
Further and Higher Education, Tadcaster Road, York. Tel:
0904 704141 or write to John Apps, course leader for
further information.

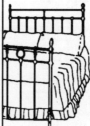